The Birth of British Radar
The memoirs of Arnold 'Skip' Wilkins OBE

2nd Edition

Edited by Colin Latham and Anne Hobbs
This edition revised by Colin Latham

Published by Radio Society of Great Britain of 3 Abbey Court, Priory Business Park, Bedford MK44 3WH, United Kingdom, in association with the Defence Electronics History Society of 18 St John's Square, Wakefield, West Yorkshire WF1 2RA.

First Edition 2006

Second Edition 2011

Digitally reprinted 2015 onwards

ISBN: 9781 9050 8675 7

Cover design: Kim Meyern
Typography and design: Mark Pressland
Production: Mark Allgar, M1MPA

Printed in Great Britain by 4Edge Ltd of Hockley, Essex

Fig 1. Arnold Frederic Wilkins OBE, 1907–1985
(Credit: Mrs Nancy Wilkins)

Contents

Abbreviations and definitions

a.c.	Alternating current.
ACO	Admiralty Compass Observatory, Slough
ADEE	Air Defence Experimental Establishment (Biggin Hill, Kent).
AAEE	Aircraft and Armament Experimental Establishment. (Martlesham 5 miles NE of Ipswich).
AMWB	Air Ministry Works and Buildings ('Works and Bricks').
ASV	Air to Surface Vessel.
CD	Coastal Defence.
CH	Chain Home. Can be confusing: (i) the UK RDF chain as distinct from possible overseas chains (CO): (ii) although the UK Chain eventually included many types of radar, the term CH often denoted, specifically, the original type of radar equipment described herein
CHiDE	Centre for the History of Defence Electronics, Bournemouth University (the organization "Friends of CHiDE" was renamed "DEHS" in December 2002)
CHL	Chain Home Low. The chain of lower-looking radar stations that supplemented the original CH stations.
CRDF	Cathode-ray Direction Finder.
CRT	Cathode-ray tube.
CW	Continuous wave (an unmodulated radio frequency carrier wave).
d.c.	Direct current.
DEHS	Defence Electronics History Society (In 2003, the Society's venue changed from Bournemouth University to the Defence Academy of the United Kingdom, College of Management & Technology, Shrivenham).
DF	Direction Finding (may indicate either traditional radio methods or the DF function of RDF - radar).
DSIR	Department of Scientific and Industrial Research.
EHT	Extra High Tension (e.g. kilovolts for cathode ray tubes).
GCI	Ground Controlled Interception.
GL	Gun Laying.
HF	High Frequency (originally also used instead of RF for Radio Frequency). In modern use the HF band extends from 3MHz to 30MHz.
HMSO	Her Majesty's Stationery Office.
HT	High Tension. The d.c. supply to anodes and other valve electrodes.

IF	Intermediate Frequency (in superheterodyne receivers).
IFF	Identification Friend or Foe.
LT	Low Tension. The filament or heater supply to valves.
MAEE	Marine Aircraft Experimental Establishment (Felixstowe).
MB	Mobile Base (transportable CH stations and prefix for CH transmitters, e.g. MB1, MB2 etc.).
NPL	National Physical Laboratory (Teddington).
PO	Post Office, or GPO, General Post Office (formerly responsible for telecommunications).
PPI	Plan Position Indicator.
pps	Pulses per second.
RAE	Royal Aircraft Establishment (Farnborough).
RAL	Rutherford Appleton Laboratory.
RDF	Radio Direction Finding (cover name for early radar).
RF	Radio frequency.
RRS	Radio Research Station, (Ditton, near Slough).
RSGB	Radio Society of Great Britain.
SSR	Secondary Surveillance Radar.
STFC	Science and Technologies Facilities Council.
TRE	Telecommunications Research Establishment.
VHF	Very High Frequency (30 to 300MHz).

Preface

Part 1 - from First Edition

At no time in its history did Great Britain face a greater threat to its continuing existence as an independent power and civilized nation than in the summer of 1940. Hitler and his chiefs of staff, having used their forces to overrun and subjugate almost the whole of Europe including our nearest neighbour, France, were determined upon the invasion of England. Detailed planning of the operation, named Seelöwe (Sea Lion) was to be completed by mid-August and implemented as soon after as possible. The Führer, evidently not known for his willingness to be guided by his senior staff, had nevertheless accepted their wisdom on one point: that the plan could only succeed with the assurance of German air superiority. Only then might the German navy succeed in shepherding the invading Nazi troops across the Channel.

Thus the first essential prelude for invasion fell to the Luftwaffe whose task was to destroy the RAF by all possible means including aerial combat, the bombing of airfields and destruction of aircraft factories.

In retrospect it is noteworthy that this early phase of the war was taken remarkably calmly in England. While there was no hiding the fact that aircrew of the RAF were daily risking and giving their lives in the summer skies above the southern counties, it was only later that this period became known as the Battle of Britain and its significance appreciated fully.

The RAF, outnumbered by intruders (highly skilled during the Spanish Civil War), won by the very narrowest of margins. Hitler's plan was shelved, thwarted for ever, and Britain was saved. For this deliverance all credit is due to the RAF and it is appropriate to recall the words attributed to the German fighter ace, Adolf Galland, 'The British had an extraordinary advantage, which we could never overcome throughout the entire war: radar and fighter control.'

The story of the birth of British radar and its integration into Fighter Command has by now been well told, not only by some of those then closely involved but also by successive historians. That Britain took steps to develop radar in time for the war was due to the vision of those whose names are now famous: Rowe, Tizard, Dowding and Watson-Watt; but its realization as a defence system came from the efforts of scientists and engineers drawn from the Civil Service, universities and selected industrial concerns. From the handful of assistants around Watson Watt in 1935, the teams of radar workers grew to many thousands as the war progressed; their numbers included brilliant scientists of the day, many of whom later gained high honours and international fame.

In these pages we read the story of radar from the one who, under Watson-Watt, was the very first of that talented throng. From his calculations in 1934 and his setting up of the 'Daventry Experiment' in 1935, all else followed.

The memoirs of Arnold Wilkins, written in 1976 and deposited in the Churchill College Library, Cambridge, expand significantly upon his earlier and shorter wartime report lodged in the Public Record Office under Ref: AIR20/195. In that wartime account

Wilkins makes it clear that he was not the originator of the idea of using the re-radiation phenomenon for the purposes of radiolocation. In other words he did not claim to have invented RDF, later known universally as radar. Nevertheless, as readers may judge from this later account, his influence upon the early development of the British radar defence system was outstanding and much is owed to his technical leadership.

The later memoirs, presented herein, have been available for inspection at Churchill College for thirty years. Nevertheless, it was felt by the committee of the Defence Electronics History Society that the growing interest in the development of radar in the Second World War justified publication in a readily available form. The committee is grateful to Mrs Nancy Wilkins for her encouragement and permission to publish her late husband's memoirs and for the approval of Allen Packwood, Director of Archives, Churchill College at the University of Cambridge.

Our source document-Arnold Wilkins's manuscript-was divided by him into twenty eight sections, individually titled and numbered. All of those sections have been retained in their entirety and their titles are included as sub-headings within our divisions into nine chapters. Thus Wilkins's record is intact and his original order has been preserved.

For minor explanations we use footnotes on the relevant pages. Longer explanations are in the form of italicized notes at the end of each chapter.

Colin Latham and Anne Stobbs (December 2005)

Part 2 - to Second Edition

In preparing a subsequent edition to an existing book, as in the present case, it often happens that the names of organisations originally mentioned have changed in the meantime. This has been a continuing aspect of radar history from the end of the 1939-45 war. To take one example, two of the major companies then producing radar hardware were Metropolitan Vickers, Manchester (Metrovick) and British Thompson Houston (BTH), Rugby. After the war they both became known as AEI (Associated Electrical Industries) and, after their radar departments had become established at Leicester, they became part of Marconi Radar Systems Ltd. Moreover, the latter had itself already been absorbed into English Electric, both being parts of the General Electric Company (GEC). In more recent years, following the death of Sir Arnold Weinstock, head of GEC, Marconi was split up and sold off with the defence radar interests being taken up by British Aerospace where the radar archives, after a complicated series of moves, now remain.

Thus keeping track of archive material often becomes complex as it is handed on but the typical progression outlined above is not confined to industry: official Government departments are good at it too! The original wartime radar work by Arnold Wilkins was begun by an extension of the Radio Research Station (RRS), Datchet, an outpost of the National Physical Laboratory (NPL). In the course of peacetime that work eventually came under the Council for the Central Laboratory of the Research Councils (CCLRC) and was so when the first edition of this book was published. Now, however, the relevant archives have become the responsibility of the Science and Technology Facilities Council (STFC) Swindon, but are held at the Rutherford Appleton Laboratories (RAL), Chilton.

Consequently, readers may notice changes between 1st and 2nd editions in, for example, the acknowledgements of the sources of illustrations. I have done my best to update and correct these where necessary but apologise in advance for any errors that may have slipped though a net possibly having, still, a few undetected holes in it.

In preparing this second edition my renewed contact with post-war ex-members of the Radio Research Station has served to confirm how it came about that Arnold Wilkins was moved to compile his memoirs of early radar development from 1935 onwards. It has been made clear that without the admiration, encouragement and insistence of one post-war RRS Director, J A Ratcliffe, FRS, these memoirs - the very core of this book - would never have been written by the self-effacing Wilkins. Lest such pressure be attributed to local gossip, possibly embroidered unwittingly, I have included, immediately before Wilkins's memoirs, a copy of the note in the Churchill College Archive Catalogue which records the matter dispassionately.

Colin Latham (January 2011)

Acknowledgements

Acknowledgement is made, with gratitude, to the following individuals for their encouragement and kind help during the preparation of this second edition: Mrs Nancy Wilkins[1] , Mrs Margaret Taylor, Mrs Gillian Evans, (respectively widow, daughter and niece of Arnold Wilkins) as well as former Radio Research Station Scientists, Dr Paul Dickinson, Dr J W King, Professor E D R Shearman, Mr R W Smith, Mr G W Gardiner; and to Mr Donald Tomlin (formerly of ADEE). Also to Sarah James of the Rutherford Appleton Laboratory (RAL), Mr Ken Wilkinson of British Aerospace (BAE), the archivist of the late Douglas Fisher and to Mr Dick Green (DEHS), for assistance in the compilation of successive drafts.

Illustrations are attributed individually as appropriate.

Fig 19 is a small reproduction of 'The First Step', a painting by Roy Huxley especially commissioned in 1985 by Marconi Radar Systems Ltd to commemorate the half century since the Daventry Experiment of 1935 in which Arnold took the leading part. The original painting was presented to him at a ceremony held in his honour by the chairman of the company, Vice Admiral Sir Philip Watson KBE. It is reproduced here by kind permission of BAE.

Following Arnold's demise in 1985, his widow kindly loaned the painting to Marconi Radar Systems to permit 500 high quality prints to be produced. Some became gifts to surviving wartime radar participants, but the majority were eagerly purchased at national radar reunions, the proceeds being donated to the RAF Benevolent Fund

---

[1] Deceased January 29th 2011

Foreword

Following the publication in 2006 of 'The Birth of British Radar', readers have requested fuller information about the life of Arnold Wilkins both before and after his vital contribution to the development of radar in WW2. It has also been suggested that, of the vast range of radar technology and equipment introduced into service during the war years, that attributable to Arnold himself might be identified as far as possible. These two objectives, plus additional comments and illustrations relevant to wartime radar development, form the expansion into this second edition. Whereas I prepared the original book jointly with Anne Stobbs, this extension is my work following Anne's unforeseen death in April 2008.

Two points about terminology:

Firstly, the word RADAR. Although this word appears throughout this book, from the title onward, such general use can be anachronistic since it was not known in this country until adopted from the USA in 1943. Here it was at first called RDF (radio direction finding) this being thought to be sufficiently vague to hide its purpose.

However, to the surprise of many working on secret RDF, the government announced in 1941 that we had a system of 'Radiolocation' which seemed like a good word although no hints were released about its operation. 'Radar', a palindrome, cleverly illustrates the essential two-way nature of the system and was sometimes, at first, taken in error to be a contraction of 'Radio Direction and Ranging'. That works, but is wrong, the original being 'Radio Detection and Ranging'. It was felt most convenient to standardise, in this book, with the now universally accepted 'radar'.

Secondly, an elusive hyphen. To use, or not, a hyphen in Watson Watt's name depends on the period implied by the context. At first Robert Alexander Watson Watt, he adopted the hyphen when receiving his knighthood in 1942 thus becoming known as Sir Robert Watson-Watt.

The main and most important element of this book, as in the first edition, is the personal record of radar development in Britain, described in Arnold Wilkins's own words. His work remains complete and unchanged including his Introduction.

A F Wilkins

a summary of his life from birth to wartime

Colin Latham (January 2011)

Early life

From what has already been said and written, it must be evident that Arnold Wilkins was a character of great talent coupled with humility and a subtle sense of finely-tuned humour. Further, from what can be gained of his background and upbringing, it appears that the credit for this attractive nature can be attributed to his typically wise choice of excellent parents. Arnold's father, John K Wilkins (1877 - 1960), was born in Bollington, Cheshire, some dozen miles south of Manchester, where his own father was a policeman until he moved into Manchester to become a dairyman and grocer. From that non-academic but eminently respectable start the young John Wilkins took advantage of the various literary and scientific groups then available in Manchester and, at age 14, was described as a 'school teacher' in the 1891 census. He went up to Oxford in 1896 as a 'non-collegiate student' (less expensive than college undergraduate fees) and eventually gained degrees of BA and BSc in physics. He also took pleasure in studying literature and languages becoming a proficient reader in both German and Italian. He continued working as a science master in Manchester until, in 1911, he accepted the important appointment of headmaster at the Chester City and County School. Having wed Louisa Jones in 1903, they then settled in Chester with their two young children, Edith Louise aged seven and Arnold Frederic, five.

From that point onwards, 'Louise' and 'Fred', as these children were then apparently known, grew up through childhood together in the Wilkins family home in Chester. Much later in his life as a married man, Arnold (to revert to his first name), would, from time to time, regale his own family with the remarkable story of how his initial entry to school in Chester was officially delayed. From what his widow, Mrs Nancy Wilkins, has told me the situation was as follows:

'There came, in Chester, a day when it was discovered that a boy of five was not down on any school register. This needed investigation so a suitable man was sent to the Wilkins home to make enquiries. The door was opened by the father and the visitor asked, 'Is your little boy unwell, Mr Wilkins?'

"No, he's very well, thank you"

"Then why is he not in school?"

"Oh, come and see", and with that they passed into another room where on the floor, face down, and studying a large family atlas, was a small boy. The visitor was used to children so he said "Hello, Arnold, do you like maps?"

"Yes", came back the quick reply, "but what is this place here called Paris and this river?"

"Oh, that's the Seine" - and so the conversation went on with never a hesitation. The visitor also caught sight of some pages from a notepad by the side of the book all in very good handwriting for a five-year old. Further up he saw plenty of numbers as well.

He turned to the father and said, "Well, there is no doubt that he is very advanced for his age. I think the best thing is to allow this to go on for now but the minute he is seven he must go to school".

Arnold later became a pupil at the Chester City and County School despite his father being the headmaster there. This, in theory, was an unusual situation which neither particularly relished but evidently it worked well. Good sense exercised on both sides avoided possible difficulties for father and son.

Arnold appears to have been a happy child, benefiting from his father's encouragement during his education and much given to reading with a growing interest in engineering through building Meccano models. As for many budding engineers, Meccano was more than a toy if taken seriously and could provide useful practical experience of basic mechanisms and structures. He is said to have disliked maths homework which he managed only slowly, sometimes avoiding it almost entirely by seeking aid from his sister who, two years older, was then ahead of him. The time thus saved on homework enabled them to enjoy playing together. There are references to some of their exploits which must have provoked parental consternation but no indications of unduly heavy or unjust punishments to follow. Incidents include Arnold's use of a vacuum cleaner to clean his sister's long hair (the effect of which has not been described but is too horrible to dwell upon!) and the time when they both engaged themselves in a 'scientific experiment' which entailed their placing a slab on top of the smoking chimney of a park-keeper's cottage. They were evidently shaken out of their research mode and brought down to earth when the furious occupant shot out of his home like a rocket, bent on seeking the culprits.

Higher education and employment

Despite his aversion to formal homework Arnold did well enough at school to be selected for further education, gaining a first degree at the Victoria University of Manchester before reading physics at St John's College, Cambridge, where he gained his second degree of MSc. Evidently his earlier distaste for mathematics was overtaken completely by his strong interest in it when applied to practical problems and he was soon to become an expert in the behaviour of the ionosphere and its effects upon the propagation of radio waves. He joined the staff of the

National Physical Laboratory in 1931 and was stationed at their Radio Research Station, Datchet, near Slough. There, he quickly took in his stride the design of radio frequency aerials and their associated transmission line systems and in particular carried out novel measurements of the phase relationships of signals picked up by different elements of direction-finding systems. He was thus well placed to assist his superior officer, Watson Watt, when the possibility of a radio 'death ray' was secretly mooted in 1935. Arnold was able to discount that approach on sound mathematical grounds but made such a convincing technical case for the possibility of aircraft detection by radio waves that Watson Watt was able to persuade the government to fund a serious exploratory programme of work.

Arnold's continuing career, from 1935 to early wartime

This, the essential core of this book, is well described by him in his memoirs included herein. Unfortunately little seems to have been recorded about the rest of his

wartime radar work but it is known that when the CH system had proved to be so successful in the Battle of Britain, he was transferred to the Air Ministry in London (following Watson Watt) and subsequently was posted to Cyprus as a scientist joining Lord Louis Mountbatten's Combined Operations Organisation. No doubt his experience in choosing the sites for the Chain Home (CH) stations would have been invaluable in making plans for Chain Overseas (CO) sites as well as his understanding of the effects of world-wide seasonal ionospheric variations upon radar and long-range radio communications. In order that he might be accorded proper authority for technical decisions amongst the higher ranking service chiefs he was afforded the honorary rank of Group Captain in the Royal Air Force.

Fig. 2. Group Captain A F Wilkins in uniform while stationed at Fighter Command Bentley Priory, Stanmore. c. 1942. Photographed in the garden of his sister's home, Edgware. (Credit: Mrs Gillian Evans)

Catalogue Note
Churchill College Archives

The following is a copy of the form in which the Memoirs of Arnold Wilkins are catalogued in the Churchill College Archives, Cambridge.

"The Early Days of Radar in Great Britain"

Title	"The Early Days of Radar in Great Britain"
Reference	GBR/10014/AWLK
Creator	Wilkins, Arnold Frederic, 1907 - 1985, physicist
Covering Dates	1997
Extent and Medium	1 volume
Repository	Churchill Archives Centre

Content and context

Arnold Frederic Wilkins was a physicist who was involved with the beginnings of radar and worked with Sir Robert Watson-Watt at the Atomic Weapons Research Establishment, Orfordness [at Orford Ness, Suffolk] and at Bawdsey.

A typescript personal account by Wilkins of the origins of radar, the work of Sir Robert Watson-Watt, the Tizard Committee, and the setting up of a coastal chain of radar stations which were important during the Second World War Battle of Britain, Wilkins was asked to write his account by John Ashworth Ratcliffe as a counter to the official account by Watson-Watt "Three steps to victory; a personal account by radar's greatest pioneer" (Odhams, London, c 1957).

The volume was given to Churchill Archives Centre by A F Wilkins in December 1977.

Introduction

by Arnold F Wilkins

The purpose of the following pages is to give a personal account of the initiation and development of radar (or RDF as it was then called in Great Britain) from February 1935 to the setting up of the Coastal Chain of stations which later played such an important part in the Battle of Britain. My qualification for attempting this task is that I was the first member of Sir Robert Watson-Watt's staff at the Radio Research Station, Slough, to become involved in this work having been consulted by him immediately after his talks with H E Wimperis which gave rise to the whole of the subsequent work on radar.

My work during the above period was concerned almost entirely with those stations later known as CH (Chain Home) and also with the beginnings of IFF up to the proposal of IFF Mark III. I was, of course, present at all the early discussions at Orfordness and Bawdsey in which were proposed other possible applications of radar such as the control of anti-aircraft guns and searchlights, airborne apparatus for facilitating fighter interception, ship detection, passive devices for jamming radar (subsequently called 'window') and others.

An important feature of this period was that all those of us employed at Orfordness and later at Bawdsey were under great pressure, often unreasonably, to produce results quickly as the Services' requirements for radar were extremely urgent. This pressure mounted after the summer of 1938 when many of us were involved in siting and installing stations with largely 'home-made' apparatus. It was never possible to give proper tests to a prototype Chain station as would be customary in normal times; the so-called Final Chain aerials were built from the drawing board and they were tested in actual Service use. It was fortunate that they performed as well as they did.

The Birth of British Radar

1

The Background

Work at the Radio Research station

At the beginning of 1935 I was employed as a Scientific Officer at the Radio Research Station of the Department of Scientific and Industrial Research situated in Ditton Park, Datchet, near Slough. The station was quite small; the number of staff was about 30, of all grades. The annual expenditure was correspondingly limited and the need to economize was constantly impressed upon us by the then Superintendent, Robert Alexander Watson Watt[1].

In view of subsequent events it will not be irrelevant to state the nature of the work on which I was engaged in early 1935. Some years previously, J Hollingworth had begun an investigation at the Station of the characteristics of high frequency propagation at oblique incidence and on his appointment in 1933 to the Chair of Electrical Engineering at Manchester College of Technology I asked Watson Watt if I could take over some of his work. He gave me a non-committal reply. Just before Hollingworth's departure to Manchester, however, Watson Watt requested me to consider how best to measure the angles of incidence at the ground of HF signals received from New York on the transatlantic telephone circuit. These measurements, he explained, had been requested by the Post Office and Hollingworth had been preparing to make them with the loop-and-vertical-aerial method. Watson Watt pointed out to me that this method was insensitive to change of angle in the range expected and some better means was required. I remember that he concluded this conversation by saying that Post Office officials considered that generally speaking the Station was capable of obtaining reliable results but took an unconscionable time in doing so and he would therefore be expecting some speedy action on my part in this investigation.

I considered two methods of angle measurement. The first, the principle of which had been used earlier by Friis of Bell Telephone Labs, was to measure the phase difference of the e.m.fs produced in two similar aerials spaced apart along the great circle between transmitter and receiver. The phase difference is proportional to the sine of the angle of incidence of the waves, but adequate rate of change of phase with angle of incidence can be obtained by judicious use of aerial spacing.

Another method considered was also inspired by Friis who was then measuring angles of incidence by comparing amplitudes of the e.m.fs produced by two similar horizontal aerials at different heights set up normal to the direction of arrival of the signals. The two aerials were connected each to its own receiver and the receiver outputs operated pen recorders. Recorder deflections were equalized with the two aerials at the same height above ground and they were then set at the operating heights. No report or paper by Friis had at that date been published and I decided that, as a first move, I must derive an expression for the e.m.f. produced in a horizontal aerial at any height above ground by a horizontally polarized wave at any angle of incidence. In doing this I simplified the work by assuming that, over the range of angle of incidence which I thought would be involved (i.e. $60°$ - $90°$), the ground would act as a perfect conductor. I was interested to discover that, while the e.m.f. in the aerial varied with its height, the phase always led by $90°$ on that of the incident wave at the ground under the aerial, i.e. it was independent of height above the ground. It was apparent that there was a standing wave system in the vertical plane in which the two aerials would be situated. I had heard of this result before and went to show my calculations to Hollingworth. He pronounced them wrong but without indicating where. Barfield was next consulted and, after considering my work, pronounced the result correct. I then discussed my findings concerning both methods with Watson Watt saying that an advantage of the second method was that, using a cathode-ray tube comparator technique, no phase angle measurement would be necessary as with the first method but only the inclination of a straight line to the axes of deflection of the cathode-ray tube. On the other hand the calculations I had made showed that, while maximum aerial height of more that 150 feet would be needed with the second method, the first method could be used with aerials of quite small height. It was this consideration that settled the method ultimately used, for the station could not afford the higher aerial masts.

The apparatus used for subsequent measurements employed a cathode-ray comparator for enabling the phase difference between the aerial e.m.fs to be measured from a photograph of the ellipse produced on the cathode ray tube. This involved a considerable consumption of photographic paper and, to overcome this drawback, I thought it would be better if a direct method of phase measurement could be devised. With the help of E C Slow, my assistant in the HF work, a continuously variable phase-shifter working at signal frequency was developed and this was inserted in the transmission line from one of the aerials. If the receiver ends of the transmission lines were paralleled and then connected to a receiver it was possible, when receiving a single down-coming ray, so to adjust the phase-shifter that the input to the receiver was zero. From the phase-shifter reading the phase difference between the aerial e.m.fs could be found, having determined the reading when the e.m.fs were in phase, e.g. when receiving from a local source equidistant from each aerial.

The drawback of the phase-shifter technique in practice will not be gone into but it was found that the phase shifter itself worked stably and well.

Watson Watt is approached by Wimperis about death rays

As stated earlier, the annual sum provided for the work of the Station was very small and this had a retarding effect on the programme. It could hardly have been this shortage of funds but rather the fact that he was an economical Scot which caused Watson Watt to use the leaves of the daily desk calendar to send requests and memoranda to the staff. On one afternoon early in February 1935, I returned to my office from the hut in which I was making my HF experiments to find one of these calendar leaves on my desk. After the lapse of 41 years I cannot remember the exact words of the request it brought from its signatory 'S' (Superintendent) but it read something like this: 'Please calculate the amount of HF power which should be radiated to raise the temperature of eight pints of water from 98°F to 105°F at a distance of 5km and a height of 1km.' Whatever the exact wording of the question, it seemed clear to me that it concerned the production of fever heat in an airman's blood by a death ray and I supposed that Watson Watt's opinion had been sought about the possibility of producing such a ray. I cannot now recall if it was before or after I had made the calculation that I saw Watson Watt who confirmed my supposition and told me that he had been invited by H E Wimperis, Director of the Scientific Research at the Air Ministry, to advise on whether the generation of a death ray by radio means was a practical proposition. Wimperis himself considered such a ray to be impossible but was seeking an outside opinion because at the Air Ministry he had received several proposals for such devices from inventors and, indeed, reports of their existence had appeared in the press.

My calculations showed, as expected, that a huge power would have to be generated at any radio frequency to produce a fever in the pilot of an aircraft, even in the unlikely event of his body not being screened by the metal casing of the fuselage. As the greatest power output obtainable at the upper end of the HF band was then a few tens of kilowatts and the gain in an array of manageable dimensions about 20dB, it was clear that no radio death ray was possible. I said all this to Watson Watt when handing him my calculations and he replied, 'Well then, if a death ray is not possible, how can we help them?' By 'them' he meant the Air Ministry or RAF. I replied to the effect that we knew that Post Office engineers had noticed disturbances to VHF reception when aircraft flew in the vicinity of their receivers and that this phenomenon might be useful for detecting enemy aircraft. I am quite certain that no mention of the desirability of devising a detecting scheme had been made in our conversation up to that point; it seemed the obvious thing to consider after the death ray had been ruled out. I remember Watson Watt interrupted me while I was making these remarks and suggested that some calculation to establish the magnitude of the phenomenon would be useful.

It is of interest that when the existence of RDF was disclosed to the public in 1942 and Watson Watt was named as the inventor, he told me he had thought of using radio waves for aircraft location before 1935 while attending a demonstration of sound locators at the Air Defence Experimental Establishment, Biggin Hill, and had put his ideas to Dr W S Tucker, the Superintendent. He asked me to seek confirmation of this but Tucker had no recollection whatever of it. Dr E T Paris who at the time of the alleged proposal was a senior member of staff at ADEE[2] also had no recollection of Watson Watt's suggestion. I think it was likely that the idea was spoken of in a light-hearted manner which carried no serious conviction and was quickly forgotten. It is certain that Watson Watt could not then have had anything more than the haziest idea as to how radio waves could be substituted for sound waves in the detection of aircraft. This I consider was supported by the fact that, during my conversation as reported above, he made no mention of ever having considered the matter previously and I was also by no means certain that he knew of the Post Office observations.

At this point I should explain that I was familiar with the Post Office work referred to through experience at the Radio Research Station in 1931, the year in which I took up my duties there. My first work concerned the propagation of VHF waves by way of the ionosphere and, before beginning the real work, I had to obtain a suitable receiver for what was then a relatively unknown frequency band. When I had acquired a few receivers I took them to Colney Heath, near St Albans, where the Post Office had the receiving station of an experimental 60 MHz circuit, the transmitter of which was at Dollis Hill. At Colney Heath these receivers were compared in performance with the Post Office receiver. While the comparisons were being made I learnt from A H Mumford, the P O engineer in charge of this VHF work, that a rhythmic variation of signal strength occurred from time to time and that it coincided with the presence of aircraft from de Havilland's aerodrome at Hatfield not far away. He regarded this disturbance of the signal as a nuisance but neither he nor his colleagues made any suggestion that the phenomenon might be of use in the sphere of air defence. While it could be stated with some truth that Mumford missed his opportunity to invent radar in 1931, so did those members of the Radio Department at the RAE who must have read the Post Office report on the Colney Heath work; and so, also, did the writer who, although his interest was aroused, failed to look further into the matter until so requested by Watson Watt in 1935.

Once again I must admit inability to remember just what Watson Watt asked me to work out. It was something like this: 'An aircraft is flying at a distance of 10km from a radio transmitter T of 1 kW radiated power and at a height of 5km. Calculate the field strength produced at the position of T by energy re-radiated by the aircraft as a result of its "illumination" by waves radiated by T'. Watson Watt gave me no other information. In making the calculation my only difficulty was in deciding the value of what one would now call the 'echoing area' of the aircraft. In those days it was common in

---

[2] Air Defence Experimental Establishment (Biggin Hill)

dealing with aerial problems to think in terms of 'effective height' and so, to simplify the problem, I decided to assume that the aircraft behaved like a half-wave dipole, the effective height of which was well known. I took two cases. The first assumed that transmitter T radiated horizontally polarized waves and that the wing span of the aircraft behaved as a half-wave horizontal dipole. There seemed to be some justification for this if the aircraft were a monoplane and, even in the then more likely case of a biplane, the wings could, with a little imagination, be considered to be something like an ellipsoid, the radiating properties of which were also known. This 'half-wave' assumption automatically settled the wavelength for which the calculation would be made as we were specifically interested in bomber aircraft and their wing-span was then about 75 feet.

The second case assumed that the aircraft radiated like a half-wave aerial in the vertical plane. There seemed less justification for this assumption than the previous one especially in the case of the biplane; in the monoplane case I thought the fuselage and wheels might act like a fat vertical dipole. This second case implied the use of vertically polarized waves of shorter wavelength than in the first case.

In the calculation for Case I the operating wavelength was taken to be 50 metres and, in Case II, 7 metres. In both cases I realized at the outset that, as the aircraft structures were 'fat' radiators, they would be flatly tuned and that their re-radiation properties would not fall off rapidly about these wavelengths.

In both cases the calculations were quite straightforward and both showed that the received field strength was, to me, surprisingly large, with the vertical polarization showing a small advantage over the horizontal.

In Watson-Watt's Three Steps to Victory (Odhams Press 1957) he says, (page 83) that the question he posed to me was: 'Assuming that the wing span of a big bomber can be represented by a single horizontal wire, what current would be produced in the wire by radio waves...the wavelength used being twice the span...?' It might be thought from this that I received a written request in the terms quoted and that Watson Watt had decided that the aircraft was to be regarded as a half-wave aerial. From what I have already stated, this was not the case. I received no written request on this occasion and the method of working out the problem was left entirely to me. I mention this in the interests of accuracy: I do not claim any credit for the half-wave assumption which, in any case, was a pretty obvious one.

Explanatory notes for Chapter 1

This chapter shows how Arnold Wilkins had become an authority on the behaviour of radio waves and aerials through his work at the Radio Research Station which he had joined in 1931. He was able to predict results by accurate calculations and to confirm performance by scientific measurements.

The work of the station had been revealed in 1933 by HMSO's publication of The Cathode-ray Tube in Radio Research authored jointly by Watson Watt, J F Herd and L H Bainbridge-Bell. That fine book, reprinted in 1935 and again in 1941, was unclassified and thus available to all. It explained the techniques by which the cathode-ray tube—then rarely encountered outside scientific laboratories—could be used to great advantage in radio direction-finding.

The book also described the methods by which pulses of radio waves were transmitted to the ionosphere and their echoes detected to measure its height. Clearly, the Government had acted wisely in consulting Watson Watt and appointing his team to the task of developing a radar defence system.

2

The Principle is Proved

The Daventry Experiment

After considering my calculations for some time, for the results seemed surprisingly favourable, I went to report to Watson Watt. He also was surprised at the results but, after a cursory examination and finding no obvious errors, began to consider what he could tell the Air Ministry. We considered what transmitter power could be generated on 50 metres wavelength and what methods could be adopted for fixing the position of the aircraft after detection. We had no doubt at all, even at this first conversation, that the method of range measurement would be by the use of pulses and that directional measurements of azimuth and elevation could be made by techniques existing at the Station. All these suggestions were contained in Watson Watt's memorandum to the Air Ministry of February 1935, which was later considered at the first meeting of the Committee for the Scientific Survey of Air Defence. This committee, under the chairmanship of Sir Henry Tizard, consisted of Professors A V Hill and P M S Blackett, H E Wimperis, and with A P Rowe (Air Ministry) as Secretary.

Up to this point I believe I was the only member of the Station staff 'in the know' but J F Herd[1] the Officer-in-Charge, must have been informed soon afterwards. It was Watson Watt, however, who told me that his memorandum had received favourable reception by the Tizard Committee and that they were recommending that facilities should be placed at his disposal for demonstrating aircraft location along the lines set out in it. Very soon afterwards Watson Watt told me that, although Wimperis was prepared to accept the validity of our calculations and to proceed with the recommendations of the Committee, the Air Member for Research and Development, Sir Hugh Dowding, had requested a demonstration of the ability of aircraft to re-radiate energy in the amounts suggested by the calculations.

The ensuing discussion began by considering how the Station's ionospheric sounding transmitter could be modified to provide a suitable demonstration. This transmitter generated pulses of 300 ms duration and its peak power was not known with certainty but did not exceed 1 kW. To modify this transmitter to generate suitably short pulses at high enough power to enable an aircraft echo to be displayed on a receiver was quite impossible in the time suggested (10

---

[1] J F (Jimmy) Herd, Watson Watt's deputy at that time.

days) and we rejected the idea quickly. I then suggested to Watson Watt that for this purpose it was not necessary to demonstrate a pulse echo but to prove that some signal of useful magnitude was being re-radiated at a worthwhile range. For such a purpose CW radiation could be used and it could be generated by an existing transmitter working on a wavelength of about 50 metres.

During my HF propagation work I had noticed that the Daventry short wave broadcasting stations of the BBC were receivable at Slough and that during anti-cyclonic weather their strength and quality was quite high and there was no fading. That waves were being bent down by the atmosphere was proved by the fact that high grade bearings of the correct value were obtained on an Adcock direction-finder and the angle of elevation as measured on my apparatus already described was very small. In investigating this effect I had collected some information on the Daventry transmitter and knew, in particular, that there was a station GSA[2] on the 49 metre band working on an array of horizontal dipoles and directed southwards. It was this station which I had in mind when making my suggestion to Watson Watt and I went on to suggest that we could set up an installation like my angle-of-incidence equipment but with means of suppressing the strong ground ray and so display on the cathode-ray tube any re-radiated signal from an aircraft flying preferably along the axis of the beam

Fig. 3. Sketch by Arnold Wilkins, photographed by Dr J W King
Annotation reads: 'Approximate lay-out for experiment performed on
26 February 1935 near Weedon, Northants - A F Wilkins' (Credit: BAE Systems)

[2] GSA: Official designation for Daventry's short-wave transmission

of GSA. I proposed to use my phase-shifter in the ground-ray suppression scheme. All this apparatus was ready and serviceable and would only need some aerials which could be made up in a few hours.

Watson Watt accepted all these ideas *in toto* and requested me to start at once to prepare the equipment for test. In leaving him on this occasion I said, 'These activities are going to arouse the curiosity of the Station. What must I say when people ask me what I am doing?' 'Oh,' said Watson Watt, 'just say you are doing a DF experiment.' The next day I started loading the apparatus into the van and was spotted by Barfield who was in charge of the DF work at the Station and who immediately posed the dreaded question. I knew it would be useless to tell him that I was going to do a DF experiment but I did so nevertheless, expecting that he would suspect something of a confidential nature and be astute and considerate enough not to bother any further. This, fortunately, is just what happened.

Before leaving the Station for a site near Daventry it was arranged (by Herd) that a Heyford bomber would be provided by the RAE[3] and it would fly up and down the GSA beam on the morning of February 26th 1935 at a height, as far as I can remember, of 10,000 feet.

It now remained to find a suitable site on or near the axis of the beam on which to set up the aerials and test the whole equipment, after which I was to notify Watson Watt where the site was so that he could find it the next day when he drove down from London with an Air Ministry representative.

The apparatus taken in the van was a twin-channel comparator (CRDF) with signal inputs provided by two horizontal half-wave aerials set up on light poles at a height of about 12 feet. The aerials were connected to the receivers by twin flexible cables and were to be spaced about 100 feet apart along the line to our transmitter. In one of these cables was to be included the phase-shifter which would, of course, be tuned to GSA's frequency. The grids of one pair of corresponding valves in the IF amplifiers were to be commoned (connected together) and, by a suitable adjustment of the phase-shifter, the signal produced by the direct wave from the GSA would be neutralized. Any re-radiated signal from the Heyford would thus show as a line on the cathode-ray tube.

The driver of the van, Dyer, and I arrived in the area near Weedon which I had previously selected by map and we were lucky enough to find a suitable field which the owner was prepared to let us use. We installed the aerials and decided to risk leaving them in position while we found a hotel for the night. After dinner we returned to the rather muddy site to test the apparatus on the transmission from GSA which was due to close down at midnight. Fortunately the aerials were intact.

The whole test had been arranged in such a hurry that I had forgotten that it would be dark when the preliminary tuning up of the receiver would be done and no provision of lighting in the van had been made. The HT and LT supplies

---

[3] Royal Aircraft Establishment

to the receivers were batteries of accumulators and all of these had to be connected correctly as had also the dry battery HT supply to the cathode-ray tube. The only electric lamp in the van body was found to be not working and could not be repaired quickly; thus it became necessary to make all the numerous connections with the sole aid of lighted matches. The result of this was that the receiver was not operating until 11.55 p.m. and in the remaining five minutes I was just able to adjust the apparatus satisfactorily.

When we came to leave the site that night we found that there had been a keen frost while we were struggling with the battery connections and the mud had frozen so hard that the van could not be moved. Luckily Dyer found a spade in the tool locker and we were able to dig ourselves out. Once again leaving the aerials standing we returned to our hotel.

Next morning on arrival at the site I felt very relieved to see the aerials still unharmed. When all was connected up GSA was tuned in and the adjustments we had made in the darkness of the previous night were found to be satisfactory. When loading up at Ditton Park I had optimistically included a unit to enable the second detector current from the comparator to operate a siphon recorder so that we should have a permanent record of any signals re-radiated from the aircraft. I set up the siphon recorder but, for some reason which I cannot recall, I failed to test whether the whole apparatus was working properly and this I subsequently regretted. It may have been that soon after tuning in that morning Watson Watt and the Air Ministry observer, A P Rowe, arrived and in the ensuing proceedings I forgot to make the check.

We did not have to wait long for the Heyford bomber to appear. On its first approach it flew well away to the east of us and no re-radiated signal was detected. The second approach was nearer the beam axis but still some way off and this time rhythmic beating of the re-radiated signal with a small direct signal allowed through the receiver was noted. As the aircraft subsequently flew off to the south good beats were observed and, calculating from the time interval from the airspeed requested (100 mph), we estimated that we had followed the aircraft for about eight miles.

In his *Three Steps to Victory* Watson-Watt says 'Rowe and I (not, so far as I remember, showing any sign of elation) bade goodbye to the demonstrators...and drove off briskly Londonwards.' From what I can remember of the occasion this lack of visible excitement was true of the visitors and of myself but, inwardly, I was highly elated and not a little relieved that, after all, the calculations I had made were not far off the mark and, knowing how rudimentary the receiving installation was, much better results could readily be obtained with better facilities. I realized we were 'on to a good thing' for air defence. I could not, however, disclose any of my thoughts to Dyer who was not in the secret and who had been sent away to a remote corner of the field during the test. I was also very relieved that the apparatus had worked so well after its long journey. The only fault that developed during the travelling was that a wire became disconnected in that part of the apparatus which would have worked the siphon recorder. This was not discovered until an attempt was made to record the beats observed on the oscillograph. It remains a disappointment that no tangible record was obtained of this test.

Watson-Watt says in his *Three Steps to Victory* that after the test he and Rowe set off for London and were well on the way when they realized they had left Watson-Watt's nephew, Pat, behind. It is indicative of how busy and concentrated I had been before and after the test that I did not even know that he had come to Weedon with them.

In Rowe's subsequent report to Wimperis and the Tizard Committee, I remember his statement that the Weedon test was the most convincing one he had ever witnessed. Later Watson Watt and I received the commendation of Sir Joseph Petavel, Director of NPL for our work.

I never knew who asked the BBC to provide the GSA transmission. It was probably Herd who would surely have had no difficulty as the BBC Engineering Department was then, as ever, most cooperative. What cover story was used I also don't know but I was interested to note the announcement at the end of the trials, 'That completes the variable amplitude tests...'

Soon after this I saw a letter in the journal *World Radio* from a reader living in Northampton who made a habit of listening to the Daventry short wave transmissions stating that he had noticed a fluttering of signals when aircraft were near. He suggested that the phenomenon might be a suitable research for readers of the journal to take up. I lost no time in showing this letter to Watson Watt with the result that *World Radio* was requested not to publish anything further on the subject.

It has recently been brought to my notice by G B Freeman, editor of the *Chronicle & Echo* of Northampton, that in Volume 1 of the official history *Royal Air Force 1939–1945* (HMSO, 1953), it is stated that the experiment described above was performed on a warm summer day on a bare hilltop near Staverton, Northants. It will be evident from the account given here that this 'official' statement is quite inaccurate in all aspects. The success of our experiment in 1935 was such that it was hardly necessary to repeat it in the following summer at Staverton, which is situated in what would be regarded as an unsuitable position well off the GSA beam, and indeed no experiments were made at Staverton at any other time.

Explanatory notes for Chapter 2

A twin channel receiver

Fig 6. is described in the RAL archives as 'Apparatus for measuring the angle of incidence of HF signals, 1933. A F Wilkins and E C Slow operating'.Such measurements entailed the establishment of the phase relationship between signals, from the same transmission, picked up by two aerials at different heights or positions. It was the kind of measurement often undertaken in the course of research into direction-finding and radio frequency systems. The equipment shown appears to have been a fairly standard tool for such work at the RRS.

It was one such set, mounted in the Morris ambulance, that Arnold borrowed from the laboratory and took to Weedon as he has described. He called it a 'twin channel-comparator (CRDF)' which stood for Cathode Ray Direction Finder, the state-of-the-art in 1933. The equipment comprised two identical superheterodyne receivers having a shared local oscillator, this unusual feature ensuring that the phase relationship between the two RF input signals would be preserved proportionately after down-conversion.

It will be seen from the photograph that the two units, one above the other, each with three tuning dials, are the tuned RF amplifiers and to the right of them are mixers, IF amplifiers, second detectors and circuits (in white and black boxes) to

Fig. 4. Morris ex-ambulance, grandly known as the RRS's Travelling Laboratory. (Credit: STFC Rutherford Appleton Lab.)

Fig. 5. Rear view of vehicle with Wilkins seated 1933. (Credit: STFC Rutherford Appleton Lab.)

feed a single cathode ray tube in the darkened space into which Wilkins is peering The common local oscillator was in the black box (with a tuning dial) beneath the lower RF box.

One of the two receiving channels fed the X plates of the CRT and the other the Y plates. Thus the phase relationship of the two RF inputs could be assessed by observing the resultant waveform which could vary from a straight line to a circle according to the phase difference. It will be seen that a typical small bright ellipse was displayed when the picture was taken.

A host of controls were to hand for setting gain, tuning etc and on the floor can be seen some of the batteries that Arnold mentions. The entire set-up certainly made a useful piece of laboratory equipment, but it is easy to understand Arnold's concern about its arriving safely after a long road journey.

As Arnold admits, it was a 'rudimentary receiving installation' but for all that it convinced A P Rowe, the official observer to the Tizard Committee who, it must never be forgotten, had been pressing the government for years about the need for scientific solutions to the problem of adequate air defence.

Fig. 6. Receiver of the Type Used at Weedon. The receiver is a twin superhet, developed at Datchet, but used at Weedon in the Morris Ambulance, officially the 'Travelling Laboratory'. Accumulators and dry batteries supplied power for valve heaters and H.T.; also many dry cells for tube E.H.T. (possibly an electrocution hazard!). Wilkins standing.
(By kind permission of the Barry Swaebe Archive and STFC Rutherford Appleton Laboratory)

Fig. 7. A close up of the picture above showing the small elliptical trace on the screen which is referred to in the explanatory notes above

Work Begins in Earnest

Preparation for work at Orfordness

It was not long after these events that Watson Watt informed me that he had been instructed to develop apparatus along the lines proposed in his memorandum to the Tizard committee and, as the work would be of a highly secret nature, it could not be carried out at the Radio Research Station. The Committee had suggested, presumably at the instigation of either Tizard or Rowe, both of whom had worked there, that Orfordness would be a very suitable place on account of its isolation and also because flying cooperation could be readily obtained from the Aircraft and Armament Experimental Establishment at Martlesham and from the Marine Aircraft Experimental Establishment at Felixstowe. I cannot recall any specific invitation to take part in this work or being ordered to do so by Watson Watt; he probably assumed that I was keen to go on with it and in this he was right. At any rate Watson Watt, Herd and I visited Orfordness probably in late March or early April 1935 to inspect the existing facilities and to decide what renovations and additions could be put in hand.

The buildings proposed for the purpose were built during the First World War when Orfordness airfield was used for experimental work in association with Martlesham and they had not been used since 1918 or 1919 and were thus in a very dilapidated condition. Nevertheless the site could not be bettered and we therefore requested that, with the utmost urgency, refurbishing should take place of one large hut for transmitter development, three small rooms for receiver and general work in what had formerly been a sleeping hut, and that a small wooden hut should be put up at a distance from these original buildings for direction-finding experiments. In addition it was requested that two 75-ft lattice towers should be erected by the side of the transmitting hut to carry the transmitting aerial and that a further four of these towers should be built near the receiving buildings. These receiving towers were to be at the corners of a rectangle; the short sides of this rectangle were about 30 metres long so that half-wave aerials for a wavelength of 50 metres could be hung from the corners and the aerials were to be about 100 metres apart. This disposition of aerials was chosen because it was intended to use, for aircraft height-finding, the angle of elevation measuring method described in Chapter 1.

It was impressed upon the Air Ministry Works and Buildings representatives who accompanied us on that visit that the greatest dispatch was necessary and that work must be completed by mid-May.

In the intervening weeks it was decided that L H Bainbridge-Bell, Scientific Officer at the Radio Research Station, should be in charge of transmitter development and that he would be assisted by E G Bowen who had worked at the Station while a research student under Professor E V Appleton at King's College, London, and would be joining the staff as a Junior Scientific Officer in April. My own work would be on the measurement techniques (i.e. range, height and bearing) and also on the aerials (transmitting and receiving).

Bainbridge-Bell started transmitter development immediately with the assistance of G A Willis, an Assistant III, and they were joined later by Bowen. Although this initial work was done at RRS there was no secrecy problem as Bainbridge-Bell had been working for some time on transmitters for ionospheric work and the staff naturally thought that he was still so engaged. The main problems concerning the transmitter were to generate a pulse of about 10 microseconds duration and of the largest possible peak power. It should be remembered that, in 1935, the ionospheric sounding apparatus was using pulse lengths of about 100 microseconds or more with peak powers of 1 kW or less. It was known that the peak power would be limited by anode heating of the transmitter valves, cathode emission and flashover problems in the valves, and that no commercially obtainable valves were likely to be suitable in all respects for our purposes. Silica envelope valves, as developed at the Signal School[1] and manufactured both by them and by the Mullard Company, were selected for the initial experiments as it was expected that their further development to our requirements could be done under conditions of secrecy at the Signal School. Bainbridge-Bell and I visited this establishment for discussions on the problem with H G Hughes and were advised on the best type for our purposes which we described as an extension of our ionospheric work. The reduction of the pulse length appeared to be a formidable problem and remained so even after discussions with L H Bedford and O S Puckle of Cossor Limited. I cannot remember what pulse length was obtained by the time the work was transferred to Orford, but it was not less than 50 microseconds.

My own work between February and May consisted largely in planning the aerial systems to be erected at Orfordness and especially deciding how to deal with the high peak voltages likely to exist on the ends of the transmitting aerials and on the lines. I discussed aerial designs with this problem in mind with Post Office engineers at Rugby and BBC engineers at Daventry. After these talks, barrels of Post Office insulators both for aerials and transmission lines were ordered for ultimate use at Orfordness.

Little or no work on receivers was possible at RRS and it was decided to start work with a 'standard' RRS ionospheric receiver and modify this as far as practicable as work proceeded at Orfordness.

It must not be thought that unlimited funds were placed at our disposal for

---

[1] HM Signals School, Portsmouth, a department of the Admiralty with facilities for the development of transmitting valves

this development work either by the Air Ministry or the DSIR[2]. Indeed, the preparations as far as apparatus acquisition was concerned went on in much the same way as if the work were a normal RRS assignment. There was, in fact, more than a little austerity in evidence. This was particularly apparent in the provision of measuring instruments. When we left for Orfordness we had two Colebrook HF wavemeters, a few voltmeters and ammeters for transmitter use and two Avometers. In addition, Bainbridge-Bell acquired a load of condemned apparatus from the NPL which was never of any use to us and was later consigned to the mud of Stony Ditch, Orfordness. It must, however, be remembered that little specialized HF measuring equipment existed in 1935. In particular no signal generator was available and there were no impedance bridges.

Figs. 8 and 9. Two views of Orfordness showing the bleakness of the location. The top picture is of one of the huts used for early development work. The bottom view is a beach scene. (Credit Douglas Fisher Archive)

The move to Orfordness

When the buildings at Orfordness were ready for occupation, the move from Datchet began. The equipment collected together was taken in RAF lorries and the staff followed by road.

Those leaving for Orford on 13 May 1935 were L H Bainbridge-Bell (SO), A F Wilkins (SO), E G Bowen (JSO), G A Willis (A3), A Bullard (Mechanic), and A J Muir (Laboratory Assistant). In addition J E Airey (A2) and R A J Savage (Carpenter) assisted in the removal and initial setting up at Orford.

It was a perfect spring day in Ditton Park and I felt reluctant to leave. The next day, at Orford, when a start was made on unloading the apparatus and ferrying it across the river Ore to Orfordness, the good weather broke and the work proceeded in torrential rain, hail and thunderstorms but the apparatus and stores were, nevertheless, transported and stored without damage. Although Air Ministry

[2] Department of Scientific & Industrial Research

Fig. 10. Crown & Castle Hotel in Orford. Venue of frequent meetings with Watson Watt (Photograph taken in 1992 Credit: Douglas Fisher Archive)

Works had done well on the preparation of the old buildings and had built a hut for the DF of a better quality than we were used to at Datchet, the aerial towers were in the earliest stages of erection. The contractors for this work were Harland and Wolff of Woolwich and their two erectors on the site reported that they had been battling against biting winds for weeks and their faces bore witness to the severity of the elements.

Watson Watt visited us at the end of our first week and we held the first of our discussions in the lounge of the Crown and Castle Hotel in Orford. Needless to say no strangers were ever present at these talks. It was probably at this first meeting that the question arose as to whether 50 metres was really the best wavelength on which to begin experiments. I suggested that while waiting for the aerial towers to be finished I should do some tests on aircraft on the ground to discover whether the wingspan showed a marked resonance at a wavelength of twice the wingspan. Although we were, of course, to be interested in the resonant properties of the aircraft in the air, I expected that the answer would be much the same when measured on the ground, because it would depend in both cases on the product of the distributed inductance and capacitance of the wing and that this product would remain more or less constant with the height of the aircraft above the ground. Watson Watt agreed that such measurements would be of interest and I began to consider how to make them with the apparatus at my disposal. My problem was how to measure the resonant frequency of an aircraft wing with two wavemeters and a pair of headphones! With one exception all the aircraft I measured were biplanes and my procedure was as follows. I placed one wavemeter under a wing and lightly coupled a single-turn coil to the oscillator coil of the wavemeter. From this coupling coil I ran a length of twin flex to the centre of a dipole aerial about two feet long stretched between the wing struts and by this means excited a current in the aircraft wings. About midway along the other wing I set up a similar dipole coupled to the second wavemeter. With the headphones plugged into the anode circuit of the second wavemeter it was possible to obtain a beat note with the output of the first wavemeter. Touching the metal wing of the aircraft produced no appreciable change to the frequency of the beat if the wing were well off resonance but, over the resonant band, the presence of the hand had a well-marked effect and, at the centre of the band, was enough to alter the reading of the grid milliammeter of the second wavemeter. As the coupling coil on the wavemeter affected the wavelength calibration of the instruments, a fresh calibration of the first wavelength when coupled to the wing was made in terms of the second wavemeter disconnected from the aircraft and brought alongside the first instrument. By such means it was ascertained that the aircraft wings displayed broad resonance on very nearly the wavelength expected from their physical dimensions. This same conclusion held good for the vertical structure of the aircraft.

The aircraft measured in this way were the Virginia bomber, Valentia transport and Demon fighter. At the MAEE[3], a Singapore flying boat was measured as well as the first Sunderland (monoplane) flying boat delivered to the RAF. While working on the latter aircraft the officer in charge of the flying tests (Wing Commander Wigglesworth, later Air Marshal Sir Philip Wigglesworth) offered to let me see inside the aircraft if I would tell him what we were doing at Orfordness. I remained in ignorance of the inside until 1942 when I flew to Gibraltar and back in a Sunderland! The information obtained in the experiments encouraged us to believe we were on the right lines in our thinking to date; even if the results had been different I do not think we would have been deflected from our intention to start work on a wavelength of 50 metres. After completion of the aerial towers we were soon able to put up a half-wave transmitting aerial cut for a wavelength of 50 metres and matched to open transmission lines by means of a quarter-wave transformer. When Bainbridge-Bell and Bowen were ready with their transmitter it was connected to this aerial and then began the main part of the transmitter development which was to reduce the pulse width and increase the peak power. There also arose the problem of knowing just what the peak power was; this was not satisfactorily settled until much later.

A similar aerial was installed for reception and led in to the ionospheric receiver set up about 100 yards away from the transmitter. This receiver was placed in a large wire-netting screening case at the suggestion of Bainbridge-Bell who thought that the paralyzing effect of the very strong direct radiation from the transmitter would have to be minimized by all possible means; later work showed such precautions to be unnecessary.

At this stage of the work we had a transmitter consisting of a self-oscillator using two silica valves type NT45 in push-pull with HT provided by an x-ray transformer and diode rectifier using modulation on to the grids. The valves were run either at their rated filament current and HT voltage or a little higher. The pulse duration was probably around 50 microseconds. The receiver itself was an unmodified ionospheric set with a bandwidth of 100 kHz. The timebase on the cathode-ray tube was modified by Willis to give a sweep time corresponding to a target range of 150 km. We worked in kilometres because we used that unit in ionospheric work. Aircraft ranges seemed better when measured in kilometres than in miles!

When operation of this apparatus began, interference from other transmissions posed only a minor problem and this seemed to me rather surprising at the time.

[3]Marine Aircraft Experimental Establishment (Felixstowe)

Explanatory notes for Chapter 3

Wilkins's reference to ionospheric receivers indicates that for this early work at Orfordness they continued, for the time being, with receivers from the RRS laboratories (as used for the Daventry experiment) until more suitable designs for short duration high-power RDF pulses became available.

The shortage of adequate facilities which made Wilkins's work so difficult has been mentioned, with much feeling, by other writers who were there at the time. Not only was there a lack of proper test gear but the procedures for obtaining materials were distressingly complex and slow.

In 'Boffin' (IOP Publishing, 1991)[4] Robert Hanbury Brown (later Professor FRS) looks back at the primitive working conditions he encountered after being persuaded to postpone his PhD studies in London to join Wilkins's team at Orfordness. Basic electrical gear comprising an Avometer, Cossor oscilloscope and an antique wavemeter hardly formed a laboratory for advanced electronic developments. Technical literature was limited to the Radio Amateur's Handbook. Fortunately both he and his colleague Donald Preist were radio hams and their practical experience proved invaluable.

Technical grades at that time were:
Lab. Assistant
Technical Assistant (TA) III
Technical Assistant (TA) II
Technical Assistant (TA) I
Junior Scientific Officer (JSO)
Scientific Officer (SO)
Principal Scientific Officer (PSO)
Assistant Chief Scientific Officer (ACSO)
Chief Scientific Officer (CSO)

---

[4] Boffin. ISBN 0-7503-0130-9, 1991

Some Success

First visit of the Tizard Committee

No aircraft echoes had been seen up to the time Watson Watt announced, during a weekend visit, that the Tizard Committee would be visiting us on 15 June. I thought on hearing this that maybe they just wanted to see the accommodation we were occupying, hear what plans we had for the future and witness any aircraft echoes, good fortune provided.

In the event, however, it appeared that they had certainly been led to expect to see some echoes and this before we had seen anything ourselves! A test flight was arranged for the Saturday afternoon of the visit and, at the appointed hour, the Valentia aircraft flew overhead at 15,000 feet regardless of the fact that a thunderstorm was brewing. Atmospherics were very strong and signal interference was also much worse than had previously been experienced. Watson Watt was observing the cathode-ray tube and claimed to see a glimpse of an echo at 27 kilometres. No other echoes were seen and we subsequently heard that the pilot had abandoned the flight because of the storm. When the flight log was received it was found that Watson Watt's observation could well have been genuine. It was decided to repeat the test the following (Sunday) morning at 7 a.m., this being the time at which, according to Watson Watt, atmospherics would be at a minimum. We all rose early on the Sunday morning only to discover on arrival at the apparatus that the storm was still in progress and, before long, it arrived back over Orford. Although the aircraft flew again for us, no trace of an echo was received. Reports arrived later to the effect that the weekend had seen thunderstorms of unusual violence. These were a useful excuse for our inability to display echoes from aircraft during a demonstration which should never have taken place. Unfortunately this was not to be the only occasion on which we were rushed into demonstrations for which we were not adequately prepared.

In view of what happened during this visit of the Tizard Committee I was very surprised to read the following paragraph in the book *Tizard* by R Clark, pub. Methuen 1965, p119.

'There had been five more meetings of the Tizard Committee by this time, and it was decided to hold the next at Orfordness. On 15th June, therefore, Tizard met Wimperis at Liverpool Street Station and travelled with him to meet Blackett, Hill,

Rowe and Watson Watt. They lunched at the "Jolly Sailors", Orford, and the whole party took the ferry to "the Island", the long peninsula on which the experimental station stood. There Watson Watt showed them a radar trace of a Valentine (sic) flying off the coast in thundery weather. "Got some lovely records up to 27 km" Wimperis noted in his diary. The following day they were out on "the Island" by 7 a.m. The tests were repeated. Even better results were recorded...After lunch, Tizard, Wimperis and Watson Watt strolled for the afternoon discussing the immense possibilities which now seemed held out by what Rowe had already christened RDF (for Radio Direction Finding).'

How Wimperis came to enter 'lovely records' in his diary I fail to understand, especially as only one glimpse of the echo was seen and that by Watson Watt alone. I do not know where Clark obtained the information that 'even better results were recorded' on the Sunday and it is very surprising that the Tizard party were discussing the immense possibilities of RDF when they had as yet seen nothing to encourage them.

One useful feature of the weekend's work was to show that action would ultimately have to be taken to minimize the effect of atmospherics and radio signals on the RDF display.

Later work at Orfordness

Not long after this Committee visit, genuine echoes were observed on various aircraft flown at our request both by the AAEE and by the MAEE. It was customary to ask for flights along the line of maximum radiation from the transmitting aerial and this took aircraft from Orfordness to Bircham Newton on the north coast of Norfolk or, in the case of marine aircraft, in the reciprocal direction. We liked the aircraft to fly at the greatest convenient height as this gave us an echo for the longest possible time. Much of the early flying was thus done at 15,000 feet as this was the greatest height permitted without the aircrew requiring oxygen. Such flights, either to Bircham Newton or to intermediate locations, were made whenever progress on the development work justified them but this flying was rather boring to the men concerned who were some of the RAF's best pilots. They naturally wanted to know what the object of it all was and had been told that we were trying to develop a method of locating aircraft by picking up the radiation from their magnetos. This was thought by one of the best of our pilots, a very intelligent Flight Sergeant, to be poor quality bluff and he set out to explode it. He argued that if, after the usual installation into all aircraft of elaborate screening harnesses on the ignition system, no noise was audible on the radio receiver in the aircraft itself, why should ignition noise be detectable at Orfordness when he was flying miles away? To prove the emptiness of our cover story he waited until another flight was requested and then flew the outward journey in the normal way but, on return, switched off his engine at 30 kilometres distance and glided the bulk of the distance to Orford. He then came to our office with his log and enquired whether all went well. I remember noting his sheepishness on this occasion but replied, as indeed was true, that all went very well. Later it was discovered by Bowen that he had returned as quickly as possible to the Sergeants' Mess at Martlesham and announced to his friends that our cover story was all bluff. As far as I know, neither he nor any other of the pilots made any further attempts to discover the true nature of our work.

After the visit of the Tizard Committee work went ahead steadily on reducing the transmitted pulse duration and increasing the power. With the lapse of time any details of Bowen's pulse-producing circuits escape me except that I remember he discovered that a Ferranti audio frequency transformer was very good for feeding the pulse on to the grid of the modulator valve without appreciable lengthening. The silica valves were overrun as much as possible and their lives were not long. During the summer of 1935 heavier filaments were introduced into the same type of valve and this raised the output considerably. It was not long before trouble began to be experienced with corona on the aerial ends. The sparking there was so strong that I recall hearing it one very calm afternoon while standing on the quay in Orford, a distance of about half a mile. We soon cleared up this trouble by soldering a copper cistern ball at each end of the aerial.

Explanatory notes for Chapter 4

Like many engineers and scientists responsible for leading new developments, Arnold Wilkins was pushed reluctantly into premature demonstrations, often with unhappy results.

His observations upon a worthless demonstration being reported in glowing terms in R W Clark's excellent book Tizard is instructive: it shows how easily, without intention on anyone's part, a story can become exaggerated or distorted unless the original source is sought and quoted. Those who study radar history have to be aware that such situations can arise, despite the best motives of all concerned. Even official reports and minutes of meetings are not always above suspicion since it is possible that, without being positively dishonest, they may have been tailored in emphasis, to some degree, for political reasons.

We have high confidence in the memoirs of Arnold Wilkins, not only because of his character and open style of writing but also because so many of his observations have been corroborated by his colleagues in the early days of radar.

The problems which Wilkins reports of atmospherics and radio signals cluttering the RDF display were later solved automatically when the decision was made to move to a higher radio frequency. At frequencies of 22 MHz and above, used by the CH stations throughout the war, interference of that kind was virtually non-existent and neither was radar performance affected to any noticeable extent by weather conditions.

Wilkins mentions the trick of soldering cistern balls to the transmitting aerials in order to cure corona discharge. Any very high voltage conductor is liable to discharge into the atmosphere under all but the driest of conditions; and this leads to sparking and radio interference. The discharges occur at the points of highest voltage—which for a dipole are at the ends—and from sharp edges where the electric field is most highly concentrated. A conductive ball at each end spreads the electric fields over larger areas so that they are less intense in any direction and corona is eliminated.

Real Progress is Made

Early receiver work

In June and July 1935, Bainbridge-Bell had made some tests to try to reduce the amplitude of the direct pulse applied to the receiver input as this was paralyzing the receiver for much longer than the pulse duration. He proposed to transmit the RF[1] pulses by open-wire transmission lines from the transmitter to receiver and there feed them into it in anti-phase to the pulses received on the aerial. It was not possible to obtain complete cancellation, however, and the improvement gained was not considered to be worthwhile. It was later found that perfectly satisfactory results could be obtained by appropriate choice of input time constants.

Little or nothing could be done to widen the passband of the ionospheric receiver to make it more suitable for the shorter pulses being transmitted. Watson Watt therefore decided to bring in F M Colebrook to design and build a new receiver suitable for pulse durations of 10 to 15 microseconds. This was in July and by September, Colebrook and McPetrie had produced a receiver which they brought to Orford for trial. The set had several stages of amplification in the IF section to counter the low gain per stage brought about by the wide band. Too many stages had, in fact, been introduced and we had to cut one of them out. Otherwise the receiver was very satisfactory and it became the pattern on which future sets were modelled. In the design Colebrook had given some attention to the time constant of the input circuit and the overloading effect present on the old receiver was now eliminated.

In the early summer of 1935 Bainbridge-Bell returned to RRS to begin the development of a cathode-ray direction finder capable of stable operation on HF. This was before any practical method of direction finding had been proposed but we were confident that something would ultimately appear and that the CRDF technique as proposed in the Memorandum would be used.

Bainbridge-Bell went away from Orford in a very pessimistic frame of mind. He was convinced that his problem was well-nigh insoluble but, by the beginning of 1936, he had produced a pair of receivers which were to be the starting point for development. The fate of these receivers is described later.

[1] Radio frequency

Counting of aircraft by RDF

A notable observation was made on 24 June 1935 while using the ionospheric receiver. During a visit by Rowe, he, Watson Watt, and I were observing the oscillograph during a test flight by a Wallace aircraft along our usual Orfordness-Bircham Newton path. On this occasion we had a camera available since W C Brown from RRS, on a visit at the time, was using one for some ionospheric recording. For some forgotten reason, we had decided to photograph various phases of the flight. We followed the Wallace out to 34½ miles and, while waiting for the echo to return on the homeward flight, spotted an echo having an unusual amplitude variation. I had seen the rhythmic variation in strength of the echo from two aircraft at the same range and saw that the variations occurring were rather more complex and said, 'That echo is probably from a formation of three'. The Wallace echo duly appeared at 34 miles and was followed back to Orfordness. Meanwhile, after we had been watching for some minutes, the echo split into what was now clearly an echo from a single aircraft and another echo beating rhythmically and thus from a formation of two. When the pilot of the Wallace arrived to give his flight log we asked him if he had seen any other aircraft during his run. By the greatest stroke of good luck he had. He had spotted a formation of three Harts one of which subsequently broke formation and went away in a different direction.

Both Watson Watt and Rowe were very impressed by this lucky observation, the former, I think, because it supported a statement he had made to the Tizard Committee about the possibility of counting aircraft by RDF, and Rowe because he realized that there was now some hope of being able to estimate the size of bomber formations. I had forgotten that Rowe had taken possession of the photographs made on this occasion and was surprised when they were reproduced in both his *One Story of Radar* and in Whiddington and Crowther's *Science at War*.

In the summer of 1935 the question arose at the Air Ministry as to whether RDF would work adequately against aircraft built with the minimum of metal. I can recall no discussion of this matter at Orfordness before we were informed that an aircraft had been bought to enable tests to be made. This aircraft, a Klemm Swallow, was entirely of wooden construction except for the control cables and, of course, the engine which itself was a very small radial (Pobjoy).

Two tests were made. A good echo was obtained at the start of the first test but it quickly disappeared at small range. We subsequently learned that the pilot had had to descend because of the 'ballooning' of the wings when the air pressure outside fell as the aircraft climbed. This difficulty was quickly overcome by making holes in the canvas covering the wings and no trouble was experienced in the second test. The echo strength was then found to be less than the other (metal) aircraft and the range of detection was about halved.

Weekend visits to Orford

At this stage of the development of radar, Watson Watt used to visit Orfordness every weekend and stay at the Crown and Castle Hotel in Orford. He generally arrived on Friday evening so as to be able to be in the laboratories on Saturday morning. On Friday and Saturday evening we frequently discussed the work in the lounge of the hotel which was not heavily patronized out of season.

Rowe visited Orford occasionally apart from his official appearances as Secretary of the Tizard Committee. Watson Watt, Bowen and I would meet in the laboratories for discussions on the current state of the work and also to answer Rowe's many questions as to what performance we expected in 'n' years' time. Rowe's main interest was in the repercussions RDF performance would have on the techniques of air defence and, in dealing with his questions, Watson Watt on many occasions made statements which seemed to Bowen and me to be little short of 'line shooting'. One of these statements related to the estimated accuracy of gun-laying anti-aircraft RDF which, in 1935, was merely a possibility. Watson Watt quoted bearing accuracies of minutes of arc and range accuracy in yards and this at a time when microwave RDF was a vision only. Was the fact that these prophesies came to pass proof of Watson Watt's remarkable foresight or was he really line-shooting?

In the summer of 1935, encouraged by the success we were having, Watson Watt, Bowen and I frequently discussed future developments of RDF which we thought likely. We discussed in particular RDF1, the chain of coastal stations which we envisioned setting up ultimately, gunnery control RDF for the Army, mobile RDF for early warning in the field and, especially, airborne RDF for night interception. These topics were considered, when appropriate, with visitors to Orfordness who began to arrive as reports of our progress circulated in defence circles. One of the earliest visitors was Charles Wright, Director of Scientific Research at the Admiralty. My main recollection of this visit was that Wright regarded metre-wave RDF as an interim device for naval vessels because, by using it, they would be acting as beacons for the enemy. He said that microwaves were essential for the future and that work would have to be done to produce powerful radiation at such wavelengths. It was undoubtedly this belief of Wright's which later led to the contract placed with Randall at Birmingham which resulted in the invention of the cavity magnetron.

Another outcome of Wright's visit was that A B Wood (of HM Signal School) was posted to Orford for two months to study in detail what we were doing. He proved to be an excellent colleague and we were all very sorry when his period of attachment ended. He was soon followed by R A Yeo and W P Anderson from the Signal School who also stayed with us for two months and then returned to develop the first ship-borne RDF equipment for early warning purposes. When this set materialized (Type 79) the transmitter bore a marked resemblance to Bowen's early set.

The staff also began to increase. At first the new recruits were sent to RRS for a period of training and indoctrination under Bainbridge-Bell. The first of the new staff were C M Minnis, S Jefferson, E E Walker and P A Hibberd.

Bawdsey is found

In August or September 1935 it became apparent that the accommodation at Orfordness would soon become inadequate and that extra space would have to be found. One afternoon in that period Watson Watt, Bowen and I set off in Watson Watt's car to explore the Martello tower at the Aldeburgh end of the Orfordness peninsula as it was thought this might provide the room required! The tower was very soon rejected and as we walked away Watson Watt asked if we had any other proposals. It so happened that at the end of our first week at Orfordness, Airey and I had gone off to explore the country round about and, by chance, found ourselves at Bawdsey Ferry. On that beautiful spring afternoon with the sun shining out of a blue sky and the river Deben lying placid at low water, we both fell in love with the place and especially with the Manor standing close to the river mouth. This seemed to me an ideal spot for the research station if ever we should have to leave Orfordness. Unfortunately, however, the house was occupied and so were several houses on the estate. Before leaving Bawdsey we ascertained that the manor belonged to Sir Cuthbert Quilter who also owned other large houses in the district.

It was this visit that I remembered as we drove away from Aldeburgh and I told Watson Watt that I could show him the ideal place but that it might not be for sale. He decided nevertheless to see it and we set off immediately. I remember that journey well because we were riding in a 15 hp Daimler which Watson Watt had just bought. As we drove along I said to him, 'I see

Fig. 11. Aerial view of Bawdsey Manor (1937)
(Credit: Douglas Fisher Archive)

that these cars have a fluid flywheel which permits one to go into reverse at 60 m.p.h. and all that happens is that the car rapidly decelerates and then moves off backwards'. 'That is interesting', said Watson Watt, 'shall we try it?'. And he did there and then and it behaved just as I had said!

When we arrived at Bawdsey Ferry, Watson Watt was as charmed with the Manor as Airey and I had been and he therefore requested the Air Ministry to find out whether the owner would be willing to sell it. To our delight he seemed quite ready to do this and to move into one of his smaller houses. The Air Ministry bought the whole estate for £23,000.

Watson Watt patents RDF

On one of his visits to Orford in the first week of our work there Watson Watt told Bowen and me that the Air Ministry had advised him to take out a secret patent for RDF. This he thought was rather a nuisance but he would have to comply with the wishes of the Air Ministry. He went on to ask us whether we wanted to be named as co-inventors on the patent and there was something in the way he asked the question that gave me the strong feeling that he wanted to keep us out of it. If we had been considering a scientific publication rather than a patent, I would have felt insulted to have had no acknowledgement of joint authorship and would have pressed to be included. I am sure that Bowen would have felt the same although, at that early date, his contribution had been minor. As we were merely considering a patent I told Watson Watt I would not wish to be included in authorship. Bowen, rather reluctantly, decided not to press his claim on the matter.

At a later date Watson Watt also patented IFF before any trials had been made of these devices. His patent included the passive, keyed dipole method which I claim to have mentioned to him although he denied it. It also included the powered device ultimately used but without specifying in detail how such a device was to be made. This illustrates one reason why I was scornful of patents in those early days; inventors should surely be asked to demonstrate a working model of their inventions before being granted a patent.

The first measurement by RDF of aircraft height

The big problem confronting us in those early days at Orfordness was that of fixing the position of an aircraft. It had become obvious that the measurement of range would soon become solved in adequate fashion but no suitable method of direction finding had occurred to us. That work on DF would be required was apparent from the outset and, as stated earlier, a special hut had been built for this purpose. In our discussions with Watson Watt we recognized that the difficulties stemmed from the fact that we were using horizontal aerials. A secondary difficulty was that we were always thinking in terms of half-wave aerials at the receiver so as to maximize signal pick-up and were intending to use arrays of half-wave aerials at the receiver and transmitter.

Bowen had suggested that the receiving aerial or array might be rotated continuously and the echo null (or minimum) observed on the linear timebase. This proposal was rejected as it was considered to be mechanically clumsy, but it was during discussions of the scheme that the idea of a timebase rotating in synchronism with the aerial was proposed. This, of course, was the first suggestion for a Plan Position Indicator (PPI). It was not possible to attribute the idea to any member of the trio then present (Watson Watt, Bowen and Wilkins) and Watson Watt subsequently said that it was a joint proposal of the three of us. A year or so later Bowen submitted a memorandum to Watson Watt for what he called a 'Radio Lighthouse'. This was a rotating narrow beam of radiation with a similar receiving aerial rotating in synchronism (as in the early models of the later CHL) and with a PPI on the receiver output. In the case of both the PPI and the Radio Lighthouse no further work was possible at that time.

In the absence of any proposal for direction finding, work at the receiving end of the Orfordness installation went ahead (September 1935) on height finding. Aerial towers had been built in suitable positions to enable a trial of the spaced aerial method (as described in Chapter 1) to be made. R H A Carter, who had joined the team from RRS in July 1935, and I made up a continuous phase-shifter (see page 8) and this was used with the Colebrook receiver. In the flying tests we requested the aircraft to circle round a small village at a known bearing from Orfordness so that the appropriate azimuth correction could be made to the measured phase angle. The aircraft flew at 7,000 feet and its height was measured in this first test to about 1200 feet. Soon afterwards I was asked to report progress to Watson Watt in his office at NPL. He was clearly very pleased with the results of this first height finding trial and so was Smith-Rose who was also present at the meeting. Watson Watt sensed that I was not over-enthusiastic and asked me the reason. I said that my reservations were that, in practical conditions, the azimuth of the aircraft would have to be known with considerable accuracy to obviate large height error, and a good deal of development of the apparatus would be required before it was suitable for Service operators.

The DF impasse was resolved in November 1935 by Watson Watt who, on arrival at Orford one weekend, announced that he had just thought of the crossed dipole arrangement on the train. The proposal seemed to be so simple that it was remarkable that no-one had thought of it earlier. Possibly previous consideration of the problem had been coloured too much by a desire to have a system reasonably free from polarization error, and the horizontal electric field counterpart of the Bellini-Tosi system was therefore mentally rejected. After considering Watson Watt's idea and finding no obvious weakness it was decided to try it out. Before making a test at Orford I went back to RRS where I had made a crossed dipole system for use in my HF work. This was fixed to the top of a telephone pole with one dipole vertical. It did not take long to re-erect the system with both dipoles in a horizontal plane and then, using a small oscillator coupled to a horizontal aerial which was carried round the crossed aerials, to observe the indications on a CRDF. There was no doubt from this test that the crossed dipole system was going to be suitable for our purposes. After reporting the success of the tests to Watson Watt I returned to Orfordness and, with Carter, put up a crude set of crossed dipoles between the 75-ft towers and connected them with lighting flex to a goniometer. In a subsequent test with the aircraft, satisfactory bearings were obtained and the system worked well enough to enable us to conclude that there would be no insuperable problems to overcome when a better engineered system could be installed on the higher masts we were expecting.

Higher aerial masts tried

The first calculations had shown that any improvement in performance of the detecting installation could be obtained more readily by increasing aerial height rather than by an increase in transmitter power. It was for this reason that Watson Watt, in about September 1935, had obtained Air Ministry approval for the erection of 250-ft lattice masts; two of these were to be used at Orfordness for a transmitter aerial and the third at Bawdsey Manor for reception. Up to this time we had received speedy service from the Air Ministry Works and Buildings Department, but in the provision of these high masts, as related by Watson Watt in *Three Steps to Victory*, we had our first experience of the inflexibility of the Civil Service machine.

There was a short setback on the progress of the work on these masts when it did ultimately begin at Orfordness; this was caused by the uneven sinking of the heavy concrete footings of the masts in the shingle of which the site was composed.

Before the masts were completed, A J Muir had begun the construction of a six-tier array for use with the transmitter. I gave Muir the lengths of each radiating element and of each reflector and he did the rest single-handed. When all was ready for its installation he called us out to pull the aerial up to its final position and, this being completed, we were all delighted to see how elegant was Muir's handiwork.

The single receiving mast at Bawdsey was begun as soon as the sale of the estate to the Air Ministry had been effected and it was completed in early March 1936. It had a cross of 4in x 4in timbers on top, intended to take the two dipoles for DF. The foreman of Harland and Wolff, the contractors, declared the mast completed one Saturday morning while Watson Watt, Minnis, Muir and I were present in the hut at the base. So anxious were we to discover by how much the performance of the system had been improved with the receiving aerial at 250 feet height that I volunteered to make the first ascent of the mast to install the aerials, seated in the bosun's chair made by AMWB. This chair had been designed to last a lifetime; the frame was made of one-inch diameter steel rod which held a thick oak seat and a heavy steel circular band, presumably to prevent one from falling off, and through which one had to climb before sitting down. The dimensions of the whole contraption had been arranged so that it would go through the top section of the mast, the cross-sectional area of which was smaller than that of the other two sections. Unfortunately no account had been taken of the passenger's knees and I soon found out that one had to be something of a contortionist to negotiate the top section while remaining in the chair. It was, furthermore, quite impossible to work on the aerial when the chair was at its highest point and I had to squeeze out of the chair and stand on one face of the mast while installing the aerials and connecting them to the open-wire lines which I had taken up with me. On completing the work I was not sorry to give the signal to Watson Watt and assistants to wind me down to contemplate the mess into which my beautiful grey flannel trousers had got through contact with the wet creosote on the mast. Later ascents were made with a home-made and simple bosun's chair, the top section being climbed without it.

In March 1936, at the time we began to install the receiver by the mast, Watson Watt told us that the Air Ministry were considering whether to spend more money on further concrete sound locators (I think he mentioned £100,000). He thought that if we could show that RDF could track an aircraft to a range of 100 km, no further concrete mirrors would be built. There was then a rush to see whether the Orfordness transmitter/Bawdsey receiver combination could give this performance.

It was stated earlier that Bainbridge-Bell had returned to RRS to develop a cathode-ray direction finder for ultimate use on RDF. By March 1936 he had arrived at the position of having two receivers which he was just starting to test. Unfortunately he was still very pessimistic about the ultimate outcome as he considered stability of performance of receivers at 20–30 MHz to be unlikely. It may have been this pessimism which caused him to hand over one of these receivers without a fight when he was approached by Watson Watt for a receiver to be used in the experiment at Bawdsey.

This test was performed in March 1936 after Bainbridge-Bell's receiver had been set up. A single Hart aircraft flew as usual at 13,000ft from Orford to Bircham Newton, a distance of 108 km, but this time we asked the pilot to continue across the Wash to Skegness and then return on the same path. Minnis and I observed at Bawdsey and were able to attain a range of 130 km with position finding all the way.

I reported this satisfactory result to Watson Watt and it is possible that it resulted in the scrapping of the project to build more concrete locators and it may be that the existing mirrors on the Kent coast were also then discarded.

Another change in operating frequency

The 250-ft high aerials used at this time were designed for use on 13 MHz. It had been found that signal interference and atmospherics on the original frequency of 6 MHz were very heavy at times and the change to 13 MHz was made in the autumn of 1935. Conditions on the new frequency were better but signal interference was troublesome at times.

Decisions as to the working frequency were made quite arbitrarily; I know of no request for allocation being made to the Post Office then or later, and we never heard about any complaints of our interfering with commercial services. Development on 13 MHz proceeded until about October 1936 when a change to 22 MHz took place. This evolved in the following circumstances.

In September 1935 we were joined at Orfordness by H Dewhurst, a Scientific Officer from the RAE, who was asked to begin the development of a transportable RDF installation for use in mobile bases (MB). As the height of his aerials would be limited by portability requirements to somewhere between 70 and 100 feet he decided to use a frequency of 22 MHz in order to keep the main lobe of the aerial radiation pattern low. This was of course sensible from the signal interference point of view and there was relatively little commercial traffic round that frequency at the time. Dewhurst's subsequent experiments showed that 22 MHz was very suitable in that aircraft echo strengths did not appear to be significantly reduced. After the near failure of the main (13 MHz) station during the September 1936 Air Exercises, it was decided to make considerable modifications to the equipment and one of these was a change to Dewhurst's original frequency of 22 MHz, he having in the meantime selected an even higher frequency.

A test of vertically polarized waves

It had been reported earlier that the initial calculations showed that a somewhat better echo strength might be obtained on 7 metres wavelength with vertically polarized waves than on 50 metres with horizontal polarization. Trials on the shorter wavelength were made in 1935 using a transmitter of unknown power made by Bowen and with a receiver made by Carter. Vertical half-wave dipoles were used at both the transmitter and receiver stations although we had drawings for an array which had been designed for this test by T Walmsley of the Post Office at Watson Watt's request. The main outcome of these experiments, during which no aircraft echoes at all were seen, was that the clutter of echoes after the ground ray was of considerably greater extent than on the more efficient 6 MHz installation and it was these facts that made us reject vertical polarization for RDF purposes. In retrospect it was fortunate that this rejection occurred as it was found much later that, in the HF band where in 1935 reasonably high power could be generated, only poor strengths were obtainable.

A curious 7-metre phenomenon

During these 7-metre tests a curious phenomenon was observed. On the completion of one flight Carter telephoned Bowen to request the switching off of the transmitter. After some minutes the ground wave reflection still persisted on the cathode-ray tube timebase although Bowen said the transmitter had been off since the first request. Investigation of the pulse shown on the cathode-ray tube revealed that its width was no greater than that given by our own transmitter; it was accurately tuned to our operating frequency at the zero mark on the range scale and was of considerable strength. The mystery was partly solved when Carter, on leaving the receiver room, absently-mindedly switched off the light. When asked to switch on again, one lamp (an old cage-filament type) failed to come on and so did the pulse on the cathode-ray tube. We concluded that the lamp had a fractured filament and the pulse had been generated by sparking across the resultant gap. Casually scanning a copy of *The Electrician* a few weeks later, I noticed an article by a contributor who had observed the same phenomenon and attributed it to sparking as we had done.

Transmitter development

While tests were being conducted using the 250-ft array at Orfordness, certain shortcomings of the transmitter began to manifest themselves. During flights it was noticed that the echo strengths suddenly dropped due to a change of frequency. On one such occasion a visit from the Tizard Committee was in progress and I was demonstrating an echo from the test aircraft to Professor Blackett and was feeling very pleased with the quite high signal-to-noise ratio seen. Suddenly there was a big drop in strength which I could not recover by re-tuning. Blackett knew the transmitter was in an early stage of development and no harm was done on this occasion.

These transmitter frequency jumps were caused by tight coupling of the transmitter oscillatory circuit to the transmission lines in order to obtain maximum power to the aerial. Excessively tight coupling put the oscillator into a critical state when some transient effect, such as a change in impedance of the transmission lines, caused it to jump frequency. Bowen blamed 'my' lines and aerials for the trouble and even went so far as to claim large losses in the lines (which were open 200 lb copper wire supported by standard Post Office insulators designed for similar lines). The obvious solution was to insert an amplifier (or a buffer) valve between the oscillator and output to the lines but Bowen would not accept this. No change was made until Bowen's transfer to full-time work on airborne RDF (RDF2) in the spring of 1936 when J H Mitchell was given the transmitter work. Unfortunately he had no previous experience and his oscillator and amplifier set was not a practical proposition. On his transfer to other work the transmitter problem was given to H Larnder whose efforts soon produced a set the output of which he gave as 25 kW peak pulse power. A good deal of argument occurred about how to measure the output power. Bowen used a resistance potential divider across the output terminals of the set and with a cathode-ray tube measured the voltage across part of the resistance. He claimed powers of up to 100 kW. Larnder tried several methods but finally settled for the well-known one in which the transmitter power is applied to a strip lamp placed alongside a similar lamp supplied from the mains. The power necessary to heat the filament of the mains lamp to the same brilliance as the other lamp enables the RF power to be obtained.

From the results gathered from aircraft echoes we concluded that '100 Bowen kilowatts equal 25 Larnder kilowatts'.

Larnder was later joined by Whelpton and between them they developed a transmitter which was subsequently used by Metropolitan Vickers as the basis for their MB1 transmitter that was installed at the early CH stations. Whelpton had several of his sets made in the Bawdsey workshops and these were used in the first five (Thames Estuary) CH stations.

Explanatory notes for Chapter 5

The ideal radar receiver would differ from those used for ionospheric research at RRS in two main respects: a wider bandwidth to cope with much shorter pulses and the ability to withstand the very high pulse input from a local radar transmitter. It should be sensitive so that weak long-range echoes were detected; yet it should be resistant to damage from the transmitter pulse and, following it, quickly return to near-normal sensitivity so that short-range echoes were not missed.

The possibility of paralysis obviously concerned Bainbridge-Bell but, as Wilkins says, it was mitigated by attention to details in the circuit design. Further receiver work, including preparing the specification for A C Cossor Ltd, contracted to make CH receivers for the whole of the Chain, was done by professional receiver designer Sidney Jefferson, who soon joined the team from EMI.

For normal (non-radar) DF receivers it had become usual to employ push-pull input stages, responding only to balanced inputs from a symmetrical aerial array. Unwanted in-phase signals picked up on both input lines would be cancelled out, ensuring that a sharp DF null was obtained. In discussion after the war, Jefferson said that was not the sole reason for push-pull input stages on standard CH receivers because co-axial cables from the aerials had become available. Push-pull, he said, had been retained mainly because it was yet another measure helping to check the strong transmitter pulse, each of the two input valves being driven, alternately, into grid current by every half cycle of the input waveform.

Watson Watt's idea of crossed dipoles worked well for DF as did Wilkins's vertically-spaced aerial scheme in which target heights were assessed by comparing the amplitudes of signal from aerials set at different heights above ground. The next chapter tells how this arrangement, on 22 MHz, was first used before becoming the standard system for CH. After the war Watson Watt wrote that, in retrospect, he wished it had been possible to provide the RAF with the more technically elegant cathode-ray direction finding (CRDF) system. He had been driven along by the urgency of the work and his own oft-quoted observations that the best solution would take too long. Nevertheless, radar operators found the CH receivers, with their goniometers, highly satisfying to use and enjoyed honing their skills. That enthusiasm was a factor in the success of CH.

Accurate measurement of a pulse transmitter's peak power is not always easy. As pulses become shorter, with faster edges, so the chance of stray pick-up by test gear—causing false indications—becomes greater. The lamp method described measured a transmitter's average power from which peak power could be calculated if the pulse width and repetition rate were known. Precise knowledge of the latter factors must have been difficult with the limited test gear available and was probably a main reason for uncertainty in the results.

Radar Defence Recognised Officially

Decision to build a Thames Estuary Chain

By December 1935, after seven months' work at Orfordness, we had developed a transmitter of 100 kW (nominal) peak pulse power which worked with a pulse width of about 15 microseconds. The receiver was adequate in gain and bandwidth. Performance on aircraft range-finding with this equipment was such that on a single aircraft flying at 7000 feet, detection could be achieved at 70 km to an accuracy of half a kilometre; the corresponding range at 15,000 feet flying height was 85 km. Ranges to which aircraft could be followed were somewhat greater. These results were all obtained using 70ft masts. A crude direction-finding system had been tried and there seemed to be no reason why a properly engineered system should not perform well. In addition to measuring range and bearing, height had also been measured by a system which required considerable development. Such was the situation when, on 19 December, we were told that the Treasury had sanctioned a chain of five RDF stations for use in the defence of London.

A recommendation had been made previously (September 1935) by the Air Defence Sub-Committee of the Committee of Imperial Defence that, as progress in the development of RDF had proceeded much faster than expected, a chain of stations should be built to cover the coast from the Tyne to Southampton and it was presumably this recommendation, modified as regards the cover to be provided, which now received Treasury approval. In retrospect this is amazing since no prototype RDF station existed to convince the Treasury that the proposed chain of stations would give value for their quite considerable cost. That the money was forthcoming at such a comparatively early stage in the technical development was clearly indicative of the urgency with which RDF was required and also that the Air Council had obviously accepted the advice of the Tizard Committee that there were no practical reasons why RDF should not perform successfully as set down in Watson Watt's Memorandum.

It was particularly remarkable in the case of the recommendation by the Air Defence Sub-Committee as the apparatus was then in the earliest stage of development and, in particular, no means had yet been proposed for direction-finding without which it was thought that position fixing would have to be performed by range-cutting using adjacent stations, a method liable to ambiguity if several aircraft were present in the operational area of the station.

By the date of the Treasury approval mentioned the crossed dipole method of direction-finding had been proposed but, by the time the design of the Estuary Chain began, it seemed that little reliance was being placed on the accuracy of this DF method. This is not surprising as what little experience had been obtained with it was confined to the very crude method at Orfordness and, somewhat later, to that at Bawdsey referred to on page 36. For the Estuary Chain it was decided to provide both DF and range-cutting facilities while, for height measurement, the aerial layout would permit the use of the horizontally-spaced method of elevation finding.

The technical requirements for the stations were that they should be as high as possible above sea level to give the best possible range of detection but that there should be an adequate amount of reasonably flat land on the seaward side of the station, as required by the elevation-finding method.

A spacing between stations of about 25 miles was thought to be adequate to give a reasonable overlap of operational areas.

Early in 1936 Watson Watt requested me to consider the siting of the stations having these requirements in mind. Bawdsey was to be the most northerly station and it would be provided with one 247ft timber transmitting tower; two similar receiving towers were to perform range, direction and elevation measurements. The next station southwards would be provided with one transmitter tower only as it would be used for range-cutting with Bawdsey or the next station southwards. The third and fifth stations were to be like Bawdsey while the fourth would transmit only. The 'transmit-only' station did not need to be on flat land.

Proposals for the sites of the four new stations were made by me from a map search with help from Minnis. Watson Watt gave his approval to the proposed sites and I went to see them with representatives of the Air Ministry Works and Buildings Branch. They were all found to be technically satisfactory and readily acquired except for the site next to Bawdsey which turned out to be a golf course. An excellent alternative was quickly found at Great Bromley.

The five stations of the chain were: (1) Bawdsey, Suffolk, (2) Great Bromley, Essex, (3) Canewdon, Essex, (4) Dunkirk, Kent and (5) Dover, Kent.

Although the range-cutting technique was to be used on this chain no serious efforts were made to study in detail how it was to be used in practice; it may be that we had faith in the success of the crossed dipoles and were looking forward to the scrapping of range-cutting.

Range-cutting died a slow death partly due, I think, to the invention by a Corporal Chapman, one of the early RAF trainees for RDF duties, of a procedure subsequently referred to as 'The Chapman Scheme'. This was towards the end of 1936. The scheme involved the provision at DF-equipped stations such as Bawdsey, Canewdon and Dover of two cathode-ray tubes for the operator to observe. One would display echoes from its own transmitter and the other from the adjacent transmitter-only station. The operator had to turn his goniometer and notice the two echoes, one on each tube, which attained minima at the same goniometer setting. It was hoped in this way to resolve ambiguity. The position of the aircraft giving rise to the two echoes would thus be found in terms of the ranges read on the tubes and the distance between the two stations. As the direction finder was not required to give bearings its accuracy was of little importance.

The Chapman scheme was quite attractive in the situation then existing and it would doubtless have been used in the Chain had it not been found that DF and ranges gave adequate plan position information. I do not recall any test of the scheme or, indeed, of plain range-cutting.

When the Great Bromley transmitter was put into operation after lengthy delays in building the aerial tower, we frequently received its direct pulse at Bawdsey and noted that it was subject to small scale but irritating jitter as observed on the cathode-ray tube. In anticipation of the Chapman Scheme, R J Dippy produced his 'Spongy Lock', an electronic flywheel, which he introduced into the timebase circuit of the cathode-ray tube displaying the Great Bromley signal. By the time this circuit was perfected we were too busy preparing for the September 1936 Air Exercises to test the Chapman Scheme.

It was decided by Watson Watt that wooden self-supporting towers would be used for supporting both transmitting and receiving aerials and a height of 247 feet was chosen. I do not remember who designed these towers but it was probably Mr Garnish of AMWB who was responsible for liaison with the contractors on the design, and F E Lutkin of RRS was also involved. The contract for their erection at all stations was awarded to Messrs C F Elwell who had been building wooden masts and towers since the earliest days of radio. When construction began it soon became apparent that no standard means of erection existed and that the foremen at each station were responsible for working out their own methods. I think this was partly the reason for the slow progress of the building.

Explanatory notes for Chapter 6

In order to generate the track of an incoming raid for the purpose of interception, a series of plots is required. With such fast-moving targets it can be more effective to have a rapid series of plots, albeit of modest accuracy, than highly accurate plots produced more slowly. It is pointless to spend time working out the exact bearing of a target if it has moved on by the time the answer appears. Consequently the ingenious Chapman scheme was not exploited. Also filter rooms, to which data from CH stations was reported, were able to enhance the overall accuracy of the Chain by assessing and integrating the plots from neighbouring stations. In principle—though probably rarely necessary—a filter officer could demand actual ranges of a target from two or more CH stations (as well as the normal grid reference plots) and find its position by their intersection on the plotting table ('range cutting').

Despite the Chapman scheme having been shelved, the Spongy Lock, which had been designed specifically for it, was retained as a standard feature of CH receivers. It provided an impeccable 25 Hz source for all the receiver, display and transmitter timing circuits, locked to the 50 Hz mains supply but free from transient disturbances. The elegance of the circuit has been much admired, its controlled phase-shift oscillator being known as the 'Dippy' oscillator after its designer, R J Dippy, later renowned for his invention and development at TRE of the GEE navigational system.

Failures and Successes

The 1936 Air Exercises

Bawdsey, Canewdon and Dover were to be ready for the Air Exercises of September 1936 and this presented us with a very big problem in that all the apparatus had to be built either at Bawdsey or, in the case of the receivers, at RRS. In normal circumstances one would have expected a reasonable period for testing before taking part in anything as serious as Air Exercises during which the eyes of the Air Force would be on us and failure might have jeopardized the whole future of RDF. These, however, were not normal circumstances and I think it true to say that no part of the equipment with which the Estuary Chain and the later Intermediate Chain were equipped had been subjected to the pre-installation testing normal for military equipment. The start of preparations for the 1936 Exercises marked, for me, the beginning of the period when installation and putting into operation of chain stations had to take precedence over research and development of aerials. The result of this was that the aerials, especially those for receiving on which the DF and elevation accuracy depended, were indeed the 'third best' which, according to Watson Watt's dictum, we had 'to give them to be going on with'.

The systems proposed for these Exercises were to work on about 13 MHz. Three receivers were built at RRS each equipped with apparatus for elevation finding by horizontally-spaced aerial technique. Five transmitters were built at Bawdsey. No aerial installation could be done until the towers were well advanced and in the event, progress on them was so slow that it had to be decided to operate the Bawdsey station only during the Exercises. Even there the towers were not complete on the first day of the Exercises. It had, however, been possible to construct a six-element array on the transmitter tower and a three element crossed-aerial array for the receiver. It was not possible to operate the elevation equipment as the second receiver tower was nowhere near complete.

In the receiving room, part of the Manor stables, we had installed three receivers in parallel as a 'belt and braces' move. Plenty of observers could thus be used simultaneously and were so used on the first day of the Exercises. On that particular day the first observers were Watson Watt, Dewhurst, Hanbury Brown and myself and I recall how silence reigned for a long period except for occasional range observations by Watson Watt reminiscent of his single observation at Orford during the first Tizard Committee visit. The complete absence of echoes was certainly odd and further inspection of the apparatus failed to reveal the cause. After the first afternoon's watch I chanced to look out of the receiving room window and was amazed to see several workmen sitting talking on the aerials! Although Watson Watt subsequently reported this incident as one way in which our efforts had been frustrated, it certainly did not explain the first day's failure. He also says in his *Three Steps to Victory* that workmen had to be removed from the transmitting tower and its thousands of volts. I did not hear this report at the time and, in any case, it probably did not explain the lack of initial success.

Later observations during these Exercises were made with the same receiving gear but we reverted to the Orford transmitter and 250ft array and reasonable results were obtained.

The Exercises thus proved very discouraging after all the hard work put into the preparations but, in retrospect, RDF should never have been used in that Exercise; we were nowhere near ready. It was lucky that the part played by the older equipment in the latter stages of the Exercises was enough to convince the Air Council of the value of RDF. I think Tizard was rather shaken by what had happened. I saw him and Watson Watt leaving the Manor immediately after the Exercises and I overheard Tizard say: '…and remember, Watson Watt, much depends on you.'

The April 1937 Air Exercises

(a) General

We were later told that the Chain was to take part in further Exercises scheduled for the following April (1937) and this time we were determined to put on a good showing.

The chief technical lessons learnt up to date were that the frequency in use (13 MHz) was subject to heavy interference and so we decided to move to 22 MHz on which frequency Dewhurst had been working with success. Transmitter instability was a serious problem and Larnder and Whelpton, who had taken over from Bowen on the transmitter development, were instructed to have suitable oscillator-amplifier transmitters ready in good time. On the receiving side, directional ambiguity had proved to be a source of criticism from the RAF and this had to be overcome. No height information had been possible during the September 1936 Exercises as only one aerial tower was usable; this lack had to be remedied for April 1937. I had been using open-wire (600 ohm) transmission lines at both transmitter and receiver. At the receiver the lines were transposed at frequent intervals but I was still afraid of mutual coupling between the two DF aerials and suggested to Watson Watt that the time was ripe to change to co-axial cable. He agreed, though neither of us knew where suitable cable was to be obtained.

It will be seen from the foregoing that we were all faced with a heavy programme in the following six months. My responsibilities still included all aerials and the provision of DF and elevation measurement and installation at the five stations. I was still very worried about the method of elevation measurement because of the large errors which would arise from DF errors. It did not seem possible so to improve the phase shifter that it would perform stably over a long period when required in April 1937. My 1932 method of comparing signal amplitudes in two vertically spaced aerials seemed altogether more promising, particularly as the signals in both aerials would be in phase and we could compare them with the DF goniometer by introducing suitable switchgear. This would simplify the operating process for Service operators. As one could reasonably assume that the horizontal radiation patterns of the two aerials would be the same, there would be no correction for azimuth.

The whole idea seemed too good to be true and a trial was clearly indicated. Before taking action I went to put the idea to Watson Watt, who I found engaged in conversation with T Walmsley [of the Post Office] who happened to be visiting Bawdsey at the time. As I had already guessed, Walmsley was 'in the know' though why he had been brought into the secret at that stage I never discovered. On this particular occasion his presence was very welcome as I valued his knowledge of aerials. After I had told my story, both Watson Watt and Walmsley agreed that my proposals were worth trying.

I decided that the new 22 MHz receiving aerials would use both 240ft towers; the DF aerials would be on one tower and the height system on the other and both sets of aerials would be connected to the receiver in the old stable block by co-axial cables.

In 1936 suitable types of co-axial cables for use on the towers did not exist. The London-Birmingham co-axial telephone cable used four high-grade co-axial cores made by Standard Telephone and Cables Ltd. I visited this firm to inquire whether they were prepared to supply the cores separately with suitable lead outer and learnt that this could be done. From the data supplied it appeared that, if we used the cable on the towers, the extra loading would amount to a few tons and this was out of the question as Watson Watt had learnt from AMWB that the towers were fully loaded with their own weight! Although we could not use the STC cable on the towers, an order was placed for the runs from tower bases to receiver and excellent cable it proved to be.

For the tower runs we decided to use a type of co-axial line already used in short lengths by the Post Office. Information on this came from Walmsley who had, I believe, designed it himself. It used a quarter inch diameter copper tube obtained from the Yorkshire Copper Company, through which was pulled a length of 100 lb copper wire to which were fitted cylindrical insulating beads at about 2-inch intervals. Walmsley lent us the punch which produced the kinks in the copper wire on each side of the beads and Airey copied it in the workshops at Bawdsey. The fixing of the beads to the wire was done after normal working hours by Minnis, Carter, Muir and myself with occasional help from Watson Watt. This was certainly a big job but easy compared with the making up of the line itself. When pulling the wire into the tube it was found that the cylindrical beads abraded the soft copper of the tube itself and a good deal of copper dust built up inside the line. After much trouble the same team completed the required lengths of line and installed them on the towers. This was by no means the end of our troubles with co-axial lines for these stations. Problems of one kind or another persisted until well into the war and various experts were brought in to try to solve them.

After our experience with 1/4in line we changed to 3/8in diameter tube of a harder copper and used triangular section beads of the same material as the original ones. Compressed air could now be blown through a long length of line to remove any copper dust or dirt. A few cases of short circuit were still experienced; they were ultimately traced to copper 'whiskers' which formed on the wire and became bent until they touched the tube. They were burnt off by connecting to one end of the line a mains transformer with a low voltage, high current output.

Adjustment of all aerials was hindered by lack of test instruments. No impedance bridges for our frequency then existed and I think it was only about this period that we received our first HF signal generator. Somewhat later we heard that a former EMI engineer, H G Atkins, had developed an impedance bridge for a frequency range which unfortunately finished some way below 15 MHz. I went to see him at his 'works' at the bottom of his garden in Kew and got him to accept an order for an instrument covering a band up to 30 MHz. After a very long delay the instrument was delivered and found to work up to 20 MHz only and Atkins was unable to improve on this. We had perforce to adjust the aerials as best we could without such instruments.

One problem was to ensure that the receiving dipoles were connected so that their signal e.m.fs added in phase. For this purpose I suggested using a portable, low sensitivity cathode-ray comparator like a miniature CRDF to compare the phases and amplitudes of the currents produced in the aerials by an oscillator at the end of the lines remote from the array. Such equipment was made up quite quickly to Carter's design. The signals to be compared were picked up on two small loops connected to their respective receivers by long flexible cables. These loops could be hung on to the aerials whose currents it was desired to compare and the phase and amplitudes of the currents derived from the pattern on the small cathode-ray tube of the comparator. This apparatus proved to be quite useful for lining up receiving arrays and also for investigating the matching of open-wire transmission lines.

The DF aerials were tested well before April 1937 and very good results were obtained using Larnder's '25 kW' transmitter. This transmitter fed the array through quite a long transmission line which we took pains to match accurately to the array.

For elevation measuring we used single dipoles at heights of 240 feet and 80 feet feeding in through a switch which enabled either of these aerials or those for DF to be connected to the goniometer. The system was calibrated by flying an aircraft in a straight line away from Bawdsey and at a constant height. Range and elevation goniometer readings were automatically fed into an ingenious optical converter designed by Bainbridge-Bell which gave the height directly. No azimuth corrections for elevation were found to be required. The same converter, when fed with range and azimuth, gave the aircraft's plan position (map grid reference).

Soon after the elevation system was completed, two incidents occurred by chance which greatly encouraged Minnis and me. Just before the lunch-time break one morning the transmitter and receiver were still working after a flight trial. We had been communicating with the aircraft and the receiver was in the RDF receiving room. While idly turning its knobs I picked up what I took to be signals from the daily meteorological flight at Mildenhall. The aircraft was giving its height in thousands of feet at regular intervals. I asked Minnis to notice whether the aircraft could be seen on the RDF and he picked it up at once at about 45 miles range. He then proceeded to measure its height and his measurements coincided exactly with those announced by the pilot.

The second incident occurred on another day while Minnis and I were observing the RDF shortly before closing down at midday. We noticed a large echo at about 15 miles range. Its height was measured at 20,000 feet which was greater than anything so far experienced. We continued to observe and saw that the height was slowly decreasing until the echo finally disappeared at approximately the position of Felixstowe. The echo must have been from a flying boat but the great height seemed against this conclusion. After lunch I telephoned the MAEE and was told that they had indeed been flying at 20,000 feet with a specially lightened flying boat. We told Watson Watt of both these observations and he was as cheered as we had been.

Shortly before the Exercises were due to start, Watson Watt told me that the Air Ministry was concerned about the [180 degree] ambiguity of our DF arrangement. He thought there would be serious criticism of RDF if nothing were done about this. I told him that we had been considering the problem and that in the time available, the only suggestion I could make was that reflector dipoles should be placed behind those dipoles in the DF array which were roughly parallel to the coastline. Provision would be made for opening or closing the centres of these reflectors at will. When closed the reflectors would cause an echo from an aircraft 'in front of' the station (i.e. out to sea) to increase in strength whereas an echo coming from inland would decrease.

Watson Watt urged me to try this scheme immediately and Muir lost no time in putting up the reflectors. For switches we selected those in which the contacts were made by mercury as I had previously found them to be excellent for this sort of purpose. On test the installation worked very well and no changes had to be made to the system.

With the sense-finding problem solved we now had all the essential elements of a complete RDF station except gap-filling.

(b) Gap filling

As soon as it was decided to use 250ft masts to support our aerials I realized that the minima in the vertical radiation patterns of these aerials would cause aircraft echoes to be lost at ranges depending on the flying height. This was so obvious that

I did not bother to say anything about it. The remedy was also obvious and this was to provide another, lower aerial, at such a height that its maxima coincided with the minima of the upper aerials or, at any rate, such that it radiated substantially over an arc including the minimum of the upper aerial. I had it in mind to make such provision at the appropriate moment.

I was surprised therefore when Watson Watt informed me at Orfordness that McPetrie had pointed out to him that we should be in trouble with high aerials because of these lobes and minima in the vertical radiation pattern. He (Watson Watt) spoke as though he had not realized this before. I was rather taken aback by this but told him my solution of the difficulty. In spite of this, he later claimed that this gap-filling method was a joint suggestion of his and mine.

In the Chain Stations we used two arrays at the transmitter with mean heights of 220ft and 80ft and, at the receiver, a main DF array at a mean height of about 220ft with a gap-filling aerial at about 80ft, while height was measured with these two aerials or with the 80ft aerial and another at 40ft. The actual heights of all these aerials were settled having regard to the contours of the sites.

The first time I observed an echo disappear when the aircraft flew into an aerial null was during a test done by Dewhurst and Hanbury Brown at Orfordness in 1936 on 22MHz, when the disappearance was exactly in accordance with expectations. This test was of interest to me, both in that it supported the polar diagram calculations and also because the timebase being used by Dewhurst showed the most beautiful display of back-scatter I had seen up to then.

In the course of our work we frequently had to plot polar diagrams of aerials and the overall diagram for a station when transmitting and receiving aerials were at different heights. We were also familiar with the plot of relative echo strength against range for a fixed flying height. When some experimental evidence was related to such calculations the agreement was invariably good and I concluded from this that whatever mysteries might be present in the performance of an RDF station, one could always rely on the calculations of the aerial vertical radiation patterns. This view was strikingly supported by the Luftwaffe on one occasion in September 1940 when I was observing at Pevensey Chain Station. On that occasion German bombers were approaching London by flying from somewhere south of Dieppe in a straight line passing near Pevensey and were roughly equally spaced and all at the same height over a 90-mile stretch. They were, in fact, in an ideal disposition to plot the range/amplitude relationship when using either main or gap-filler aerials. There was, unfortunately, no camera available to record this wonderful display but, from observations made, the agreement with calculations was excellent as was the efficacy of the gap-filling equipment.

When the first transmitting array on a 360ft steel tower was completed at Bawdsey it was thought advisable to measure its horizontal radiation pattern in view of the possibility of distortion due to the presence of the tower (the aerial was suspended between the upper and centre cantilevers). The measurements were made by B G Ewing in an RAF motor launch in a rather choppy sea. I was very surprised therefore when Ewing delivered what might have been the theoretical diagram for a half-wave aerial with indications that there was little scatter in his readings and this in spite of the rough sea and the fact that this was the first practical work he had done since leaving school! He saw that I was sceptical of the results but stoutly denied any 'editing' when he arrived back on land. No repeat of these measurements was immediately possible and, as flying tests indicated no gross distortion of the pattern, we let the matter rest.

Gap-filling was certainly used during the April 1937 Exercises. At the transmitter we arranged to switch the power into either the upper or lower array by solenoid-operated switch-gear remotely controlled from the receiver and a transmission line arrangement to obviate open-circuiting the transmitter output during aerial switch-over. The method developed became the standard for future CH stations.

(c) The Canewdon and Dover Stations

It has been stated earlier that these two stations were intended for both transmission and reception, i.e. they were to be complete RDF stations, whereas Great Bromley and Dunkirk were for transmission only.

Canewdon and Dover were both prepared for the April 1937 Exercises. Transmitters were built at Bawdsey, receivers at RRS but modified at Bawdsey, while the aerials were installed by an RAF party with help from Bawdsey. Calibration of aerials was done by members of my own group at Bawdsey.

I cannot remember any details of the performance of these stations during the Exercises as my whole attention was taken up with the operations at Bawdsey, but both worked satisfactorily. The performance at Dover was such that S/Ldr C K Chandler, then responsible for the operation of the RAF DF network, was moved to remark that he could not understand how that station could plot a better track on an aircraft using secondary radiation than his stations could using primary radiation. The outcome of this statement was a competition between RDF and DF and Minnis and I went to Dover to operate the RDF to observe on an Anson aircraft which was to fly to the Wandelaar Light Vessel and back. At the same time, the aircraft would transmit signals for reception by the DF network of Bellini-Tosi stations. At Dover we plotted quite a good track and 'saw' the aircraft turn at the Wandelaar and obtained a good return track. When the DF tracks were plotted they seemed to show that the aircraft had violated Belgian airspace by flying well inside that country! I gathered that the DF system was drastically overhauled after that test.

Another noteworthy observation made by us during this visit to Dover was that echoes were plotted from three definite areas in Belgium which we subsequently discovered corresponded to military airfields. We thought this ability to 'see' military aircraft flying around their base might have some operational value. The next occasion I witnessed the same phenomenon was during my stay at Pevensey already referred to when one could observe German aircraft circling their base south of Dieppe before starting on raids on London.

Explanatory notes for Chapter 7

Hanbury Brown in 'Boffin', comments on the fiasco of the 1936 Air Exercises when he was one of the observers who, in the presence of distinguished visitors invited from London, failed to observe RDF signals. It had been impossible to provide, as planned, five RDF stations for the exercises and even to get Bawdsey working in time had required preparations described as 'frenetic'. Hanbury Brown tells how, while the operators sat watching anxiously for echoes that never came, Watson Watt contrived to provide a running commentary on an event that was not actually happening at all. Disappointment and embarrassment was followed by such a late cold lunch that Air Marshal Sir Hugh Dowding was assumed to have been put off RDF for ever. However, fortune smiled and Sir Hugh was able to witness an excellent impromptu demonstration provided by the airborne RDF group using relatively small RDF equipment mounted on one of Bawdsey Manor towers. The day was saved—just.

Bainbridge-Bell's ingenious optical converter was limited to experimental versions. However, its twin objectives—the conversion of range/bearing data into Grid Reference plots, and of elevation/range into actual target heights—was achieved successfully by the famous 'fruit machine'. This was the Electrical Calculator, a concept of G A Roberts who, with Edward Fennessy (later Sir Edward), set up the first filter room at Fighter Command HQ, Bentley Priory, Stanmore.

The 'Calc' or 'fruit machine' (because its illuminated display in a CH operations room resembled that of the early gaming machines then becoming popular) was designed and fully developed by the Post Office Engineering Department. It was based on the electro-mechanical technology of automatic telephone exchanges using relays and uniselector switches. Fed by the radar operator with ranges and bearings of targets, together with their angle of elevation ('theta-h') it calculated and displayed grid reference plots and target heights. These were read off and sent by secure telephone line to filter room. The Calculator was eventually installed at all CH stations.

The CH transmitting aerials included reflectors on the landward side so that most of the radiation was out to sea. However, the modest aerial gain of about 9dB did allow enough back radiation for some targets to be seen over land. Back-front sensing dipoles for receiving solved the 180 degree ambiguity problem as Wilkins describes, and they were supplemented, on final CH installations, by similar side-sensing dipoles.

Wilkins tells how echoes would disappear as aircraft flew into gaps in the vertical cover ('aerial nulls') and how their positions agreed well with calculations. A consequence of this was that on some wartime radars on which full height-finding facilities were not provided it was nevertheless possible, on occasions, for experienced operators to give fair estimates of the approximate heights of incoming raids. This was done by noting the ranges at which signals faded—only to reappear shortly—and by reference to the station's vertical performance diagram. Wilkins's pioneering aerial work had implications beyond CH.

The Chain is Proved
Beyond Doubt

Outcome of the 1937 Exercises

The results obtained in the Exercises have been adequately summarized by Watson Watt in his *Three Steps to Victory* (pp.180-181). From my point of view it was gratifying that the systems for DF, height finding, sense determination and gap-filling had all worked well and could be adopted for any further stations which might be required. They were, in fact, used at all CH stations until their final scrapping a few years after the end of the war.

The main result of these exercises was that a decision was made to extend the Chain to cover the whole coastline from the Isle of Wight to the Tay.

I was once again asked to find suitable sites for all the stations required. The spacing of stations was settled in terms of the known performance of RDF at different flying heights and the Air Ministry requirement for a gapless RDF frontier at thirty miles from the coast for aircraft flying at 5000 feet.

The Estuary Chain was designed for optimum performance in the direction of Ostende as it was considered by the 'authorities' that, if war with Germany did break out, the enemy would never advance further than that town. This is why we arranged our transmitting dipoles at right angles to the great circle from the station to Ostende.

With Minnis's help I settled the approximate locations of the required stations and, after Watson Watt had given his approval, I set off to visit all areas and make firm siting proposals. I was accompanied by R J Struthers of AMWB Engineering Branch and an officer of the Lands Branch. It had previously been decided, largely by Watson Watt, that a 'standard' Chain Station should consist of four 240ft wooden towers at the corners of a rhombus (receiver) and four 360ft steel transmitter towers in line on the extension of a line drawn through the centre of the rhombus parallel to two of its sides. Why Watson Watt decided on the rhombus was never clear; I think he considered that interaction between receiving aerials would be reduced if that layout were used. The 360ft steel masts were selected because it would be possible to put on them arrays of similar mean height to the highest receiving aerial. AMWB had estimated that their cost would be the same as that of the wooden towers already in use (£2,400 each). The four towers were to carry arrays for different frequencies which could be selected at will as one method of countering jamming. This layout was borne in mind when site-hunting, but there was nothing magic about it and it was only possible to adopt it in five or six cases.

The sites selected for this extension of the Chain were:

To the north: High Street, Darsham (Suffolk), Stoke Holy Cross (Norfolk), West Beckham (Norfolk), Stenigot (Lincs), Staxton Wold (Yorkshire), Danby Beacon (Yorkshire), Ottercops (Northumberland), Drone Hill (Berwickshire), Douglas Wood (Angus).

To the south: Rye (Sussex), Pevensey (Sussex), Poling (Sussex) and Ventnor (Isle of Wight).

After making selections with the AMWB representatives, Watson Watt, Struthers and I visited all proposed sites and approved them all. Difficulties arose in the acquisition of land at Danby Beacon and Ottercops Moss, in both cases I think because owners feared interference with their grouse shooting!

The Ventnor station siting was something of a jest. At the period concerned it was considered unlikely that, in the event of war, there would be much air activity as far west as Ventnor, and Watson Watt and I did not regard the siting there as a very serious matter. As the site at St Boniface Down was 760ft above sea level, with an immediate drop to Ventnor and the sea, we could not resist the temptation to use it to see whether a station there was good for low-flying detection. It was, of course, realized that height measurement would be out of the question, but nevertheless, when the station came to be fitted with its aerials, a standard height-finding system was included. When the wartime RDF workers visited Ventnor CH station and found it perched on top of a cliff but equipped with height-finding gear, they had some justification in thinking the pre-war staff incompetent.

It has already been reported that the Great Bromley and Dunkirk stations of the Estuary Chain were intended for transmitting only. The success in the Exercises of the crossed-dipole DF led to the abandonment of the range-cutting proposals and consideration had to be given therefore to the future of these two stations. It was soon decided in the case of Great Bromley, which was on a flat site, that it should become a full station. Dunkirk however was on a very unsuitable site for height-finding purposes, although good in other respects. After much consideration it was decided to retain the station and extend it to 'full' status although it was realized that height-finding might be difficult if not impossible. When the final installation came to be calibrated it was found that height calibrations varied considerably with azimuth but fortunately these variations were adequately handled by G A Roberts's 'fruit machine' calculator.

Another weakness of Dunkirk came to light in the early months of the war. It was then found that echoes from the London balloon barrage were proving to be a serious hindrance to plotting over a large part of the time-base. This trouble was reported by Dowding to the Air Ministry and it was ultimately brought to my notice.

The reason for the trouble was obviously that the station was on the top of a hill which sloped away fairly steeply in the direction of London and there was an optical path to the London balloons. The echoes causing offence to Dowding were produced by the backward radiation from the Dunkirk transmitter which could not be eliminated by any practical sized reflector. I thought it quite likely that the unwanted echoes could be reduced to a sufficiently low level by radiating an equal amount of energy in the direction of the 'centre of gravity' of the barrage but in anti-phase to that from the main array. R A G Cooper and I set up a small rhombic aerial directed towards London and of an impedance such that it could only accept a small fraction of the main transmitter power, and tapped it on to the transmission line to the main array at such a point that its radiation was in anti-phase to that of the main array. After a few minor adjustments the system worked well and the unwanted echoes were almost entirely eliminated.

Further extensions of the Chain were made soon after this major extension when Prawle Point (Devonshire) and Nether Button (Orkney) were added. Both sites were selected by B G Ewing.

The allocation of frequencies for all these stations was made by me with help from E W Seward. In these days of strictly controlled frequency allocations it is amazing to look back upon the way Seward and I carried out this task. We decided what the frequencies should be in the band upwards from 22.4 MHz. We gave no heed to foreign users of frequencies in this band who might be interfered with and decided only to avoid the television and amateur bands at home. We spaced the frequencies round the chain so as to minimize mutual interference. We were aware of the possibility of back scatter, but did not then know enough about it to be able to predict its incidence and its potential to cause interference; we hoped that adjusting the time of emission of the pulse relative to that of the scatter-producing station would overcome this problem.

The frequencies so chosen were passed to E J C Dixon, who was coordinator of all the work required in the building of the Chain, and the appropriate aerials etc were in due course provided.

The final Chain never used four frequencies per station; I think the usual provision was two sets of aerials for one frequency. During the war, aerials were installed at two stations (High Street and Rye) for the highest frequencies in the Wilkins-Seward schedule (about 60 MHz) so that the general performance at these frequencies could be ascertained and, in particular, whether their ability to measure smaller angles of elevation was of value. Minnis reported that in each case performance was excellent and that height finding started at a greater range than on the lower frequency. At the time the tests were made there was not enough effort available to build aerials for these frequencies at other stations and consequently no more use was made of them.

The Munich crisis

When we started work on RDF in 1935, Watson Watt gave us until the summer of 1938 to have equipment in operational use, as this was when he expected war with Germany to start. In the event he was not far wrong. By September 1938 there were several stations working but not with the 'final' equipment. Their transmitters were MB1s, an engineered version of Larnder and Whelpton's Bawdsey set, made by Metropolitan Vickers. The receivers were by Cossor. Both these firms had been let into the secret of RDF and became responsible for the transmitters and receivers of Chain stations throughout their life.

The aerials for these stations were erected by the RAF Installation Unit under S/Ldr J W Rose and height and DF calibration were made by members of my own group. This calibration work was a heavy burden which effectively put an end to all development work on the aerials. We had, for example, plans to make a thorough investigation of a receiving aerial system as proposed for the final Chain, and, after many delays, had succeeded in completing such a system at the time the Munich crisis began. Minnis was looking forward to working on it after the crisis had passed but, unfortunately, the day after its completion the tower supporting it was struck by lightning and the whole aerial system ruined. The year or so which preceded the outbreak of war and the evacuation of Bawdsey Research Station to Dundee was so filled with work of an urgent nature for the Chain that no further development was possible.

Station calibration was originally done by flying aircraft on radial courses out from and back to the station concerned. This was quite a good method for height calibration but, for DF, not so good unless the aircraft's position could be obtained accurately by requesting it to circle a lightship. This was not often possible.

During a visit to Bawdsey in about 1938, Lord Rutherford suggested that a better method of calibration would be to use the echo from a dipole hung from a balloon flown from a ship at sea. This method was adopted with great success and used up to the outbreak of war, after which a balloon at sea would have been too vulnerable to enemy air attack. Calibration throughout the war was done by dipole-carrying autogyros.

The performance of RDF on high-flying aircraft

Up to the outbreak of war, most of the experience of the performance of CH stations had been on aircraft flying at heights up to about 15,000 feet, and ranges of detection were broadly in accordance with expectations.

During the Battle of Britain and from time to time subsequently, it was reported that performance on high-flying aircraft was poor or non-existent. Thus, in *The Narrow Margin* by D Wood and D Dempster (Hutchinson 1961), Chapter 18, it is stated that, in October 1940, 'Goering resorted to the use of fighter-bombers operating at high altitude. These tactics were difficult to counter because of the height at which the German fighters flew…Moreover, raids approaching at 20,000 feet or more had a good chance of minimizing the effect of radar observation…'

High-flying standing patrols were instituted by the RAF in the areas where these tactics were likely to be used but, according to Wood and Dempster, 'such efforts were not sufficient answer to the problem of intercepting raiders which flew too high for detection by the radar chain'.

If any investigation of this alleged weakness was made at the time it could not have shown any technical failing of RDF, for no report on any such failings was sent to the Research Establishment by Fighter Command. I know of no fundamental technical reason why performance should be poor at great heights. On later occasions, when I investigated reports of such alleged failure, the explanation was that the Filter Room at Fighter Command would not accept plots beyond a certain (medium) range and, as a result, the RDF operators took no notice of echoes at long range.

In 1942, at the request of Air Marshal Sir Philip Joubert through Watson Watt, I was asked to look into this problem again as Joubert had received complaints that the Chain was failing to report enemy reconnaissance aircraft approaching the Southampton area at about 40,000 feet. I decided to visit Poling CH station in the hopes that some useful information might be obtained there. In this I had a most remarkable stroke of luck.

On arriving in the Receiver Room I found that the stand-by equipment was in use while the main receiver had been undergoing servicing. This had just finished and the receiver was working but unmanned. I could see the timebase on the cathode-ray tube on entering the room and, even at that distance, thought I saw an echo at about the maximum range (about 150 miles). This was in fact the case and my further measurements showed the echo to correspond to a single aircraft at 42,000 feet, approaching Poling from the south-east. A good strong echo was plotted for some time and, as there appeared to be no other activity at the time, I asked the Tangmere operations room to which Poling was connected by telephone if they were to attempt an interception. The high-flying Spitfire which was sent up intercepted the Junkers reconnaissance aircraft without difficulty, but the guns jammed when the pilot opened fire. Thus ended an experiment performed with the excellent co-operation of the Luftwaffe which showed that, as expected, the RDF was working well on high flyers. Later investigations showed that the earliest possible warning of these aircraft was being lost by the rejection by the Filter room of long-range plots. As a result of this experiment, a special table was provided at Stanmore to take such plots.

Explanatory notes for Chapter 8

Wilkins's successful 1932 method of height finding by comparison of the signal amplitudes from vertically spaced aerials was also used on the later 1.5m radars for Ground Controlled Interception (GCI). The system of comparison and display was quite different from CH but the underlying principle was the same.

As Wilkins points out, it was not expected that the vertical lobes of the Dunkirk station, situated as it was, would be sufficiently predictable at all azimuths to permit reliable target height measurements to be made. However, it is interesting to note his comment that this potential defect was evidently mitigated by the 'fruit machine'. That was because the results of calibration exercises carried out on CH stations were recorded in a programme 'hard-wired' on to the uniselector switches. As a result, corrections found necessary at different bearings, either in DF or height readings, were taken into account automatically on every plot.

It must have been a relief (though doubtless an irritation) for Wilkins to discover that the reason for the lack of high altitude plots was not technical but entirely organizational. It was well known that, because of the chosen waveband and practical limitations to the height of the aerials, much of the coverage provided by CH stations was directed skywards to include altitudes unattainable by normal aircraft. However, this feature turned out to be of advantage in the late stages of the war when CH stations were able to plot the trajectories of the very high-flying supersonic V2 rockets launched against this country, thus enabling the location of the launching sites to be estimated for attention by Bomber Command.

The Birth of
Secondary Radar

The story of IFF[1]

The possibility of making friendly aircraft modify their RDF echoes in such a way as to identify themselves was considered right at the outset. It was suggested as early as the conversations I had with Watson Watt immediately preceding the writing of his Memorandum. The 'keyed resonant array' idea mentioned in that Memorandum was claimed by Watson Watt as his own idea and I have, on at least one occasion, argued with him about this. I can clearly recall in the above-mentioned discussion saying that if any aircraft behaved like the resonant dipole of my calculations, then another keyed dipole, suitably placed, should alter the strength of the received echo.

It was not possible to put this modest proposal to the test until 1937. The Army group at Bawdsey under E T Paris were experimenting with RDF for gun-laying (GL) and were having some difficulty in following the echo of their own test aircraft when others were in the vicinity. Dewhurst was having similar trouble when testing his MB apparatus. Both sets of equipment were operating on about 7 metres wavelength. Both groups decided to try the keyed dipole idea and Dewhurst agreed to fit the aircraft, an Anson, with a suitable dipole. On subsequent test no response was achieved either on GL or MB. Rowe, who by then had become Superintendent at Bawdsey, then asked me to try. I had not seen the arrangement used by Dewhurst on the Anson and did not do so before starting on my own attempt.

My plan was as follows. The Anson was equipped with a retractable undercarriage which protruded slightly from the wooden wings when retracted. As each wheel and supporting struts were of a suitable separation, I decided to run the dipole between them and, from the centre of the dipole, split by an insulator into two quarter-waves, run a length of twin cable to a motor-driven make-and-break device. The twin cable was cut to a suitable number of half-waves in electrical length so as to present a short circuit at the dipole centre when the switch was closed. In test the arrangement worked well on both equipments and continued to be used by the Army group. The installation in the Anson was done by R H A Carter who also made the switch.

With the arrival of new staff it was possible to start full-time work on IFF. The main problem was to obtain identification on the Chain frequencies which by then had been placed in the bands 22–30 MHz and 40–60 MHz.

First of all, keyed dipoles were fitted on flying boats and useful results obtained at

---

[1] Identification Friend or Foe

Bawdsey when the dipole was in the nose of the aircraft. Later, tests were made with wires hung between main and tailplanes, and it was while flying on one of these tests that the aircraft, a Scapa, crashed killing the crew and our assistant Hunter Gray. At the subsequent enquiry this unfortunate event was found to have been caused by an airframe failure and our wires were not blameworthy.

I think we also fitted a Heyford bomber with a nose dipole and achieved success. One of these tests was witnessed by Dowding who had become C-in-C Fighter Command; we heard later that he was prepared to request the fitting of the whole bomber force with dipoles.

I had observed nearly all the keyed-dipole tests up to this point and had concluded that, with a single aircraft, the effect of the keying was quite adequate as a means of identification, but that with a formation, the 'beating' of the echoes would almost certainly mask the changes of strength produced by the keying. On hearing of Dowding's proposed action, I went to see Rowe and told him of my fears and said that, in my view, we should start work on powered IFF so as to provide an amplified response from the friendly aircraft which would override any 'beating' of the echo from a formation. Rowe was certainly convinced and told me to lose no time in starting to develop a suitable apparatus.

Rowe had a habit of naming an investigation 'the most important job on the Station' and then paying a daily visit to those working on it to ensure that they were also regarding it in the same light. This powered IFF work came into this category and must have been considered of such high importance by Rowe that, in addition to putting my group on the job, he also instructed Preist and R W Taylor to work on it simultaneously.

Watson Watt, as reported earlier, had previously taken out a patent for this powered IFF idea (which seemed obvious enough to most of us) but the specification gave no recipe for the instrument to carry the idea into practice.

When instructed to undertake this work, I put Carter on to the job immediately. Apart from having taken part in all the IFF work to date, Carter was a very useful man with circuits and a fast and zealous worker. In thinking about the problem I decided that a compact but fairly sensitive receiver would have to be used to receive the pulses from the Chain stations and that the received pulses would have to trigger an oscillator working on the same frequency as the received signal and thus emit a strong pulse for reception by the Chain. I decided that a super-regenerative receiver should be small and sensitive enough, although possibly tricky to work. When handing the job to Carter I gave him a circuit diagram of an instrument he might find useful. His subsequent work certainly used the super-regenerative receiver but everything else was of his own devising.

The Air Ministry allocated a special aircraft for this work, a Harrow monoplane bomber. The problem arose as to what kind of aerial to put on it for IFF. In 1931, when helping R H Barfield in some DF tests on signals transmitted from Bristol Bulldog fighters, I had noted the 'Christmas tree' effect of the wingtip-to-tail aerials and had wondered whether the aerials could be buried in the planes or whether we could use the metal girders of other aircraft. Now I was presented with a good opportunity to try this idea without having to go through official channels. It so happened that the tailplane of the Harrow was almost exactly half a wavelength long at the Bawdsey frequency (22.7

MHz). I decided therefore to regard the fuselage as tapped on to a half-wave dipole at a voltage node and not likely to have much effect on the current in the tailplane, and so made connection to the dipole electrically by means of a Y-tap.

When Carter first took the equipment into the air it was not surprising that troubles occurred, but if the set itself did not work properly there was evidence that the tail aerial was working as witnessed by signals received at Bawdsey when Carter put the set into oscillation. It did not take him long to get his apparatus working properly and we were able to demonstrate it to Rowe's satisfaction. On one occasion when Carter was flying in the Harrow and I was operating the RDF and passing plots over the telephone to the Operations Room at Fighter Command Headquarters, I discovered a visit was taking place by Admiral of the Fleet Lord Chatfield, then Minister for the Co-ordination of Defence. As good echoes were being obtained from Carter's Harrow I passed plots on it to the Ops Room, stressing that this plane was identifying itself as friendly. This was the first time identified plots had been accepted at the Command Operations Room and the staff there saw to it that Chatfield was made aware of the fact.

Carter was the first to make powered IFF apparatus; Preist and Taylor made their apparatus work soon afterwards. I cannot recall the details of their method and did not witness any trial of it.

In the spring of 1938 I was joined by F C Williams and, at Rowe's request, he was asked to adjudicate between the Carter and the Preist/Taylor sets. He recommended the further development of Carter's set and the abandonment of the other and he, Williams, then began this development with a view to early production. He made one major addition to the set: the ability to re-transmit pulses of different widths. This facility was used to identify aircraft as fighter or coastal etc and there was a very wide pulse for distress purposes.

When Williams's work had progressed sufficiently a contractor, Ferranti, was brought in to produce a few sets to be used during the air Exercises of 1939. Several of these sets were fitted in Anson aircraft, the aerial being a copper tape fitted along the leading edge of the wooden tailplane. For the other aircraft taking part, Y-taps on the tailplanes would have been used.

I cannot recollect what results were obtained in the short period of use before the sets were hastily removed by the aircrews when fire broke out in them. When Ferranti investigated this trouble it was discovered that the reservoir capacitors across the HT supply had become excessively hot due to conduction through their unsuitable dielectric.

These first (Mark I) sets covered the lower frequency band of the Coastal Chain only. Williams then started on the development of a Mark II set to cover the whole of the Chain frequencies (22-60 MHz) and it was this set which was ultimately fitted in many thousands of aircraft during the war.

Aerials for the Mark II set were, in most aircraft, the Y-tap on the tail and such an aerial was found to work well. In a few cases difficulty was experienced in obtaining a good enough aerial using the tailplane; the Blenheim and Skua were examples of such cases, all of which were dealt with by using taps on the main plane.

The first RDF beacon

At the beginning of the war, the Research Station moved to Dundee. Early in our stay there I received a visit from a S/Ldr Lugg—a Coastal Command officer who had been associated with our work for some time. He had just visited the Coastal Command airfield at Leuchars where he had learnt that the aircraft operating from there had often had difficulty in locating their base at night or in bad weather, and he inquired whether we could help in this matter. Knowing that these aircraft were equipped with ASV working on a wavelength of one and a half metres, I asked Carter if he thought it possible to modify an IFF set to work on that wavelength so that we could set it up at Leuchars to act as a beacon. Carter thought he could do this, and as Lugg approved our suggestion, lost no time in making the necessary changes. He took the modified set to Leuchars and set it up on top of one of the aerodrome buildings and made some test flights to establish its value.

The details of the operation of this, the first ground radar beacon, now escape me but I know that it was found valuable and was still in operation when we moved from Dundee to Swanage in May 1940. It was the forerunner of other ground beacons used with considerable success, notably for assisting night fighters.

Sir Edward Appleton and IFF

Sir Edward Appleton was made a member of the Tizard Committee when it was re-formed after the resignation of all the original members in October 1936. The only suggestion of a technical character he made which came to my knowledge was of a circuit for IFF. His note on this was shown to me by Watson Watt in 1942 although it had undoubtedly been written much earlier. I was asked if it contained anything of value. It was clearly too late to consider alternative circuits when thousands of IFF sets were already in satisfactory use, unless Appleton's circuit had shown major advantages over the existing one and this was not the case.

IFF Mark III

In early 1940 it became evident that, as the number of different types of RDF and the frequency band used by them had increased, a radical change in the design of the IFF instrument was necessary. In particular, the CHL stations worked on a frequency of about 200 MHz which could not be covered in the single sweep of the Mk II set. This problem was considered by Watson Watt, F C Williams and myself and it was decided that the next equipment should work in a frequency band of its own. This implied that at each RDF installation there would have to be a separate interrogator transmitter and receiver and that the IFF display might well differ for each type of RDF.

Full-scale development of this Mk III apparatus began after the move of the Research Station to Swanage in May 1940 and I played no further part in the programme, having been moved to new work at the Air Ministry.

Arnold Wilkins, November 1977

Explanatory notes for Chapter 9

Other radar work at Bawdsey

In the last few pre-war years, while Wilkins and his team were working on high-power RDF for long-range early warning, two other groups at Bawdsey had been equally busy developing lower-powered shorter-range sets. The airborne group achieved sets working at around 200 MHz, including ASV (Air to Surface Vessel) carried by aircraft of Coastal Command. Meanwhile the Army group, working at a similar frequency, developed CD (for Coastal Defence) which, when sited at the coast, was able to detect shipping at moderate ranges. CD picked up aircraft flying too low for detection by CH and formed the basis for CHL (Chain Home Low) stations shortly to be deployed around the Chain to complement the CH stations.

IFF and Beacons

Development of IFF commenced for one straightforward reason: to ensure that echoes from friendly aircraft could be distinguished, as unambiguously as possible, from those of the enemy. That aim was achieved but it could hardly have been visualized at the time that it would lead to other applications, some being of much greater complexity.

The first of these, a homing beacon evolved from MkI IFF for aircraft approaching Leuchars, is described by Wilkins. Casually inspired and produced unofficially as it was it became the forerunner of other forms of beacon for essential navigational purposes throughout the war.

The second was the change to MkIII IFF operating in its own waveband of 157–187 MHz. Wilkins mentions how this step was considered by Watson Watt, himself and F C Williams and that the development continued at Swanage. There, an outstandingly inventive group of engineers including Vivian Bowden (later Lord Bowden of Chesterfield) worked with this same circuit genius Dr Williams (later Sir Frederick, OBE, CBE, FRS) on the development of MkIII.

After the war, research continued in various establishments and the system of interrogating an aircraft on one frequency and receiving encoded replies on another was exploited further and became known as 'secondary radar' (on the higher frequency band of 1030-1090 MHz). In its various modes it has served for military IFF and with aircraft of civil airlines throughout the world, for identification and pulse-coded communication.

Secondary radar, which demands transmission from an aircraft (to be avoided as far as possible in wartime), may be used as a ground-based surveillance and identification system for civilian aircraft in peacetime. It has two inherent advantages over normal (primary) radar which relies entirely upon the reflecting characteristics of the aircraft:

1. *Since the 'up' and 'down' frequencies are different, complete freedom from ground clutter and permanent echoes is ensured.*

2.   *Providing that the aircraft's transmission can be received at the ground station, the operational range of an SSR system is proportional to the square root of the ground transmitter's power output; but the detection range of a primary radar system is proportional to the fourth root of the transmitter power. Thus relatively long ranges can be achieved by SSR with transmitters of modest power.*

Secondary Surveillance Radar (SSR), established as a vital and essential element of modern air traffic control, is the oak tree that grew from the acorn at Bawdsey.

Addendum

A F Wilkins's original notes (1935)

The following photo-copy of a sheet of notepaper in Arnold Wilkins's handwriting, shows how, when compiling his memoirs, he jotted down thoughts as they occurred to him. The paper was found and preserved by Dr J W King whose rearrangement into chronological order - and presentation in typed form - makes a strikingly concise summary of progress in a period of only seven months in 1935. From having no radar in May, a five-station chain was sanctioned before Christmas!

Left RRS 13/5/35. Started work Bawdsey 14/5/35.
Party consisting of LH Bainbridge-Bell (SO), AF Wilkins (SO), EG Bowen (JSO),
GA Willis (A3), A Munn (LA), A Bullard (Inst. Maker), attached for many
period JE Airey (A2), RAJ Savage (Carpenter).
In July 1935 RHA Carter (A3) joined the team.
In Sept 1935 H Dewhurst (SO) was transferred from Radio
Dept. RAE but remained ... employed
up to Nov 1935 the staff from RRS (ie Radio Dept NPL)
had achieved the following:-

1. First pulse echoes from aircraft June 1935 measurement of range
2. By ... Sept 1935 had achieved detection at 40 km or more
   at 7000 feet using 70 foot high aerials (T+R)
3 In Nov obtained ... on aircraft using crossed dipoles
4 In Sept first measured height of aircraft using horizontally
   spaced aerial system
5. In July counted number of aircraft in small formation and
   saw possibility of estimating number of a/c in large formation
   we had therefore demonstrated the feasibility of carrying out all
   the items mentioned in RAWW memorandum of Feb 1935.
   In Sept 1935 (16th) Air Defence Sub-Cttee of CID recommended,
   with concurrence of Air Council, that a chain of radar detection stations
   from Tyne to Solent should now be established
   In 19 Dec 1935 Treasury sanctioned a 5-station chain covering the
   approaches to London (Bawdsey to ... Foreness)
   all this as a result of the work of RRS staff

Transcript (Re-arranged & edited to be in chronological order)

"Left RRS 13 May 35. Started work Orford 14 May 35.

Party consisted of L H Bainbridge-Bell (SO), A F Wilkins (SO), E G T Bowen (SO), G A Willis (SO), A Muir (LA), A Bullard (Inst. Maker). Attached for moving-in period J E Airey (A2), R A J Savage (Carpenter)

June 1935	First pulse echoes from aircraft and measurement of range
July 1935.	R H A Carter (A3) joined the team
In July 1935	Counted number of aircraft in small formation and saw possibility of estimating numbers of a/c in large formations
By Aug-Sept 1935	Detection at 70 km of aircraft at 7,000 feet using 70 foot high aerials (T+R)
Sept 1935	H Dewhurst (SO) was transferred from Radio Dept. RAE but remained Air Min. employee
Sept 1935	First measured height of aircraft using horizontally spaced aerial system
16 Sept 1935	Air Defence Sub-Cttee of CID recommended, with concurrence of Air Council, that a chain of radio detection stations from the Tyne to Southampton should now be established
In Nov 1935	Obtained azimuth on aircraft using crossed dipoles
By Nov 1935	The staff from RRS (i.e. Radio Dept. NPL) had therefore demonstrated the feasibility of carrying out all the items mentioned in R A Watson Watts's memorandum of Feb 1935
On 19 Dec 1935	Treasury sanctioned a five-station chain covering the approaches to London (Bawdsey to South Foreland)

All this as a result of the work of RRS staff."

The radar Chain and how it expanded

It is doubtful whether even Arnold Wilkins himself, when asked by Watson Watt to seek four more sites to complement Bawdsey, could have foreseen how rapidly the wartime chain of 'Air Ministry Experimental Stations' would grow and how extensively it would become developed with the rapid advances in radar technology.

Radar in the final years of peace

The initial five sites selected by Arnold formed the first section of long range RDF stations, all reporting their plots to the first Filter Room at Bentley Priory, Stanmore, from 1938 onwards. The plotting process, (as occasionally depicted in films and on television), was carried out by plotters (usually WAAFs), who received in their headphones plot data from CH stations which they placed on a large table map of the area using special markers which they positioned with croupier-like sticks. The plotters (recruited, for secrecy, in the early days of radar as a 'Clerks SD' for 'special duties') were connected directly to the 'tellers' at CH stations.

Grid coordinates were derived at the CH by plotting ranges and bearings on a suitably marked map, and heights were obtained by referring gonio readings to height charts. This was done manually at first but more quickly later with the Electronic Calculator. The tellers also added 'Friendly' or 'Hostile' with plot identities according to IFF interrogations. Ranges in miles, resulting from readings from the range scales of accurately calibrated cathode ray tubes were of a good order of accuracy but bearings in degrees of azimuth from goniometers could be less so. Aircraft heights also, obtained from gonio readings from aerials at different heights, could vary in accuracy. Yet as individual targets would often be seen by more than one CH station, it was possible for experienced filter officers, observing combined plots on the table, to make quick and valid decisions about the truest positions and heights of each plot before they were passed on to the operational aircraft groups. That was 'filtering'.

With their aerials directed broadly eastwards these five stations were placed so as to counter what was then seen, in the event of war breaking out, as the gravest immediate threat - attacks on London from German bombers. Those stations, becoming operational during 1938, were able, within the limited availability of the air traffic at the time, to practise their range and direction finding - and the plotting of tracks - by taking advantage of echoes from any aircraft flying in their area of coverage. It is noteworthy that at least two opportunities of special interest occurred before the actual outbreak of war in September 1939 although, curiously, Wilkins has mentioned neither of them in his memoirs.

The first was the use of radar during the 'Munich Crisis' of September 1938 in tracking the aircraft carrying the Prime Minister, Mr Neville Chamberlain, on his flights to and from Germany until his final meeting with Herr Hitler on September 30th. This was the historic occasion when, on emerging from the aircraft at Heston, the PM waved a piece of paper said to be a new agreement, signed with Hitler that morning, which he believed guaranteed peace in our time. It appeared that if Germany occupied that region of Czechoslovakia partly German-populated, Hitler would have no further territorial demands in Europe. Amidst much widespread rejoicing throughout the country a minority doubted the value of that statement and thought Chamberlain had given way too easily.

Whatever the truth of that view, there can be no doubt that the 11 month delay before Chamberlain himself- the self-confessed peacemaker - was forced to declare war against German aggression in Poland was a bonus for British radar. In that period the chain was extended by CH stations so placed that long-range early warning was provided along the obvious air routes from Germany to the UK. As Arnold has stated, his original five sites included Bawdsey (Suffolk), Great Bromley (Essex), Canewdon (Essex), Dunkirk (Kent) and Swingate (Nr Dover). He adds that following the 1937 Autumn Exercise, another nine stations - from Ventnor to Douglas Wood were authorised. (This led on, later, to even more CH stations being erected on the east coast of Scotland beyond Douglas Wood, including School Hill, Hill Head, Loth, Tannach, Netherbutton, and Whale Head plus CHL stations as equipment became available.)

Such a vast constructional feat was made possible not only by industry turning out sufficient transmitters, receivers and ancillary equipment but also by the overall radar organisation of the RAF headed by HQ 60 Group at Leighton Buzzard and its base at Kidbrooke, SE London which included installation, calibration and maintenance teams as well as equipment stores. In retrospect it appears truly remarkable that such widespread installation work, spread across the UK, was achieved in such a way that its real purpose was not revealed.

The second unusual opportunity for radar tracking by the original five CH stations, plus some of the newer east coast stations then already on watch, occurred barely a month before the war began. German interest having been aroused by their observation of so many aerial towers and masts being erected along our coastlines they decided to investigate. It was on the 2nd and 3rd of August 1939 that the giant airship, Graf Zeppelin LZ130, equipped with radio receiving equipment and carrying a crew of scientists and technicians embarked on a spying mission along almost the entire length of the east coasts of England and Scotland. The Zeppelin was not only detected by radar as the biggest echo ever seen on the CH range displays but was observed visually and photographed from the ground as well as being photographed off the Scottish coast by an RAF aircraft from Dyce (Nr Aberdeen).

This visitation by the Zeppelin caused much concern. If the function of Bawdsey and of the chain stations had been grasped by Germany then surely a first action in wartime would have been a massive bombing campaign against them. The loss of Bawdsey would be especially serious since it was not just one of the chain stations but also the centre for radar research, both ground-based and airborne. When war was declared on September 3rd 1939 an evacuation plan, already proposed by Bawdsey's Superintendent A P Rowe and agreed with Watson Watt, was implemented immediately. In the inevitable rush Dundee was picked for ground radar and Scone (Nr Perth) for airborne. Both venues were unsuitable and soon changed again but the curious fact is that the expected German attack on Bawdsey or any of the east coast stations never materialised! It was only in August 1940 that heavy attacks were made upon Dunkirk (Kent), Dover, Rye, Pevensey, Ventor and Poling, with some being very severely damaged, but Germany then refrained from further attacks on CH stations. Sir Edward Fennessy (wartime Group Captain at 60 Group) discussed this after the war with General Martini, ex-Chief Signals Officer of the Luftwaffe, and learned that Goering was unimpressed with radar and ordered that as the attacks had not put the transmitters out of action (due to prompt use of reserve equipment) no more time was to be wasted on such raids. What a bonus for the RAF!

Despite the care with which the German team had set up the spying mission they failed to grasp that we had an operational warning system. It may be regarded as providential that Wilkins's choice of parameters for CH was so far removed from what Germany had done for their own radars that they did not recognise ours even as they were being tracked. The peculiar characteristics of CH - static aerials, metric wavelengths, low pulse repetition rate - all adopted for sound reasons at the time but not replicated in later British radars for different but equally valid considerations, saved the day and very probably this country from eventual German domination.

Radar installations during the Battle of Britain

By the summer of 1940 when the Battle of Britain was at its height and Germany was hoping to overcome the RAF prior to launching an invasion from France, the radar coverage was being extended westward of Ventnor by the installation of CH stations of the West Coast type to augment the existing East Coast types. While this work was under way, approaching completion, the western parts of the UK were given immediate radar cover by a combination of mobile CH units (AMES Type 9) and the new CHLs (AMES Type 2) as far as North Wales.

Further extension of the Chain

As the war developed, many new centimetric radars working in the CHEL role (Types 30-37, 40-47 & 50-57) were installed either on new coastal sites or co-sited with existing radars. As newer radar sensors, taking advantage of improved equipment at shorter wavelengths, became available it was convenient to install them on existing sites or, if that was not practicable, on nearby sites administered from a CH. For example, Bawdsey (Suffolk) had a complete 1.5m CHL on one of its steel towers as well as several microwave radars. Conversely Branscombe CH (Devon), ran its own CHL at Beer Head some five miles away. The CH system, as set up by Wilkins and his team was more than just a chain of radars: it was also an integrated network of reporting centres all connected by high quality telephone lines to regional filter rooms of which several more were established over the UK in addition to the original at Stanmore. It was expedient, in some cases, to pass co-sited CHL and CHEL plots down the existing CH telephone lines.

60 Group was also responsible for sites and equipment for 50cm radars (Types 11 and 16) to stand in for 1.5m CHL and GCI radars if jammed (50cm being well-used by the enemy), as well as for radar-like navigational aids (e.g. GEE, Oboe, Loran) which either stood alone or shared radar sites.

The end result of all these installations, masterminded by HQ 60 Group from early in the war and continuing throughout, was that the entire coasts of England, Wales and Scotland as well as Northern Ireland and the Isle of Man, were provided with early warning of approaching enemy aircraft. CH stations exceeded 50 in number plus some 70 CHLs and numerous separate microwave and navaid sites.

By March 1945 a few UK sites had been relegated to a standby role since the focus of the war had moved to the continent. Even so, radar establishments included nearly 200 actual radar sites at home plus related establishments such as filter rooms, regional wing headquarters, research centres, training schools, repair and maintenance units. So much for the RAF, but the Navy and Army had their radar organizations too, all evolved from the early work at Orfordness and Bawdsey.

All this - within just ten years since the Daventry Experiment of 1935, when radar was un-named and unknown - was the result of much effort from many participants who deserve great credit. However, it is fair to reflect that it all became possible for two reasons: that CH was able (unwittingly) to foil the Zeppelin mission, and that it had been ready and fully operational in time for the Battle of Britain.

Arnold Wilkins at Ditton Park, post-war

It appears that Arnold's decision to return after the war to the Radio Research Station, at Ditton Park near Slough, was wise and fruitful. As Deputy Director he not only exercised his organisational abilities and thereby assisted in the administration of the unit, but also found time for personal participation within his favourite activity of researching long-range radio communication by ionospheric reflections. Of the many diverse subjects undertaken by the RRS - relevant to radio communication and electronics - this was one of the longer term and more enduring projects.

Arnold's superior was the Director of the RRS and during the period 1960-66 this post was held by Dr John Ashworth Ratcliffe CB, CBE, FRS. This scientist's experience of radar was extensive having served for most of the war as Director of both the Educational and Post-Design Services at TRE. It has been said that at the end of the war over a third of TRE's 3000-strong staff came under Ratcliffe. He was also known as an outstanding teacher of technical subjects, an ability doubtless stemming from his pre-war appointment as professor of upper-atmosphere physics at Cambridge.

The trigger for Arnold to compile his memoirs

It has been related, by those at the RRS at the time, that when Sir Robert Watson-Watt's massive volume 'THREE STEPS TO VICTORY – a Personal Account by Radar's Greatest Pioneer' was published in 1957 Ratcliffe - from his own experience and knowledge of radar - took strong exception to some parts of it. Therefore, (as mentioned briefly in the Preface Part 2) he persuaded Wilkins to prepare his own unbiased account of early British radar development and to have it lodged at Cambridge. That is what we have in this book, thanks to Ratcliffe's encouragement and Arnold's careful compilation over an extended period before passing it to Cambridge in 1977.

It has often been observed by those who worked with Arnold Wilkins that he was invariably generous in allowing others to take credit for his ideas. Readers may be surprised, therefore, to find a few gentle digs at Watson-Watt within these memoirs. We should take these at their face value and, like everything that Wilkins reported, regard them as wholly true.

However, we must not allow ourselves to conclude, from what Wilkins has written about early radar development, that Watson Watt was then anything but the right man for the job. The work had needed strong enthusiastic leadership and that he gave in full measure. It has been said that when in charge of Bawdsey Research Station he was a much-liked and benign boss. More than that, he did much to present the infant radar in the most favourable light to the Air Staff and to the Government, thereby ensuring their essential moral backing and continuing financial support.

Watson Watt's prowess in that respect was endorsed by one of Wilkins's early team, Professor Robert Hanbury Brown FRS, who wrote in appreciative terms, in his book BOFFIN, that Watson Watt was the best salesman he had ever met and who could easily have sold refrigerators to Eskimos.

Even if Wilkins has not been entirely complimentary about his wartime boss, they worked well together and both must have accepted that their roles were complementary. Neither would have been right for the other's job, but together – and with their quickly growing team of engineers and scientists – they produced the goods just in time for the inevitable war with Nazi Germany.

In his Obituary to Wilkins in The Times of 9th August 1985 Ratcliffe mentions the Daventry demonstration and adds: 'Wilkins headed a team, at the secret Research Station at Orfordness, which developed the scheme to the stage when, in 1937, it could be used operationally. As leader of the team he was always known as 'Skip' Wilkins, a title that remained with him till long after the war. At the Research Station he was personally responsible for the design of the aerials and for positioning the CH stations along the coast, ready for use in wartime.'

'At the start of the War, several university workers were brought in to the Research Station which soon developed into a much larger establishment. The newcomers were given senior posts, while the original workers, including Wilkins, were relegated to junior positions. For 'Skip', in particular, it must have been a great disappointment but he was never once heard to complain. After the War, he played a leading part in the Radio Research Station, where his career had started: there, his administrative skills were of great value and his cheerful and equitable temperament brought him many friends.'

Several ex-members of the RRS staff have kindly given their recollections of serving under Wilkins as Deputy Director after the war. He appears to have been happy there and held in high regard with his habit of inventing appropriate nicknames for individuals and his aptitude for mimicking regional accents with humorous exaggerations. Possibly he had a particularly keen ear for pitches and rhythms stemming from his violin training as a boy which must also have enhanced his enjoyment of listening to – and observing – the birds in the pond near his office window.

There were times, when the pressures of tight post-war budgeting bore heavily upon him, when he would playfully upbraid his staff for their justifiable demands for trivial items. How different for him from the comparatively easy-going finances of wartime and no wonder that, in frustration, he fiercely demanded to know if they actually ate their crocodile clips! As an experienced practical scientist he would have understood well his staff's needs for new equipment and facilities yet the system required that he scrutinise requisitions before adding his support to the inevitable expenditure, however small.

No wonder he took a gloomy view of each new demand. In that respect he began to earn the kindly nickname of 'Eeyore' but the pseudonym by which he was best known remained the time-honoured 'Skip'.

Clearly much liked and admired, his character is well summed up by Richard W Smith, one who knew Arnold closely for many years:
'Without doubt his quiet temperament and pragmatism provided the perfect foil to the highly efficient, power-driven Watson-Watt. These two, and their dedicated team, deserve this country's gratitude for having developed radar which contributed so much to the outcome of World War 2.'

Post war radar-like research at RRS

Of the select band of outstanding scientists, transferred in wartime to radar research establishments for the armed services, some became well known by the public in the ensuing years of peace for their contributions to new and exciting scientific projects. Such subjects included astronomy, nuclear power and space travel.

Although Wilkins's post-war career was not in those categories he nevertheless enjoyed some compensation in that he was able, at the RRS, to continue his interest in researching the possibilities of world-wide radio contact by further study of the phenomenon of reflections from the upper atmosphere. Much of that work entailed the building of what, in effect, were long range radar systems able to display, at selected hours of the day or night, regions of the world to which communication was possible at particular radio frequencies. His professional colleagues included E D R Shearman (later Professor) who, over a 24 hr period, took a series of long range PPI photographs of reflected transmissions at 17 MHz. Three of these are shown in Fig. 12, the displays indicating, by the darkened areas, the zones from which ground backscattered echoes are being received at the time of the observation. This reveals the likelihood of communication from the UK to those zones.

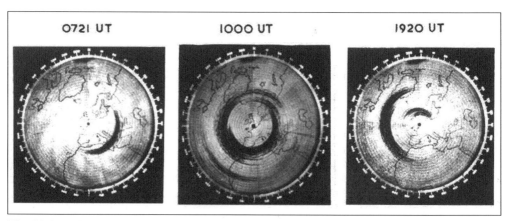

Fig. 12. Plan Position Displays of back-scatter echoes as daylight moves across Europe and the Atlantic in October 1954. (Credit: EDR Shearman)

At 7.21 a.m. communication is possible only to south east Europe. At 10.00 a.m. communication is possible in all directions. By 7.20 p.m. communication is only possible westwards to the North Atlantic, from West Africa to Greenland. (The fluttering echoes to the North are from Aurora, much studied to the present day.)

Fig. 13 shows Arnold Wilkins demonstrating to the Duke of Edinburgh a PPI display of back scattered echoes from ground areas illuminated by a 17 MHz rotating YAGI radar antenna. The system employed a modified MB2 (Mobile-Based Chain Home) 100kW pulse transmitter. The display showed directly at any time, the parts of the earth's surface over a 6000 km radius around Slough, to which short wave Radio communication was possible. The third person is Sir Ben Lockspeiser, Secretary to the DSIR.

Fig. 13. Visit of the Duke of Edinburgh to the DSIR Radio Research Station c. 1955 (By kind permission of the Slough Observer/ STFC Rutherford Appleton Lab.)

Further work made possible the recording of arrival times of pulses arriving at a remote receiver by different numbers of ionospheric reflections from a transmitter and how this pattern changed with frequency over a band 5-25 MHz (an 'oblique ionogram'). For this a stepped-frequency 100 kW pulsed transmitter and a remote transportable stepped-frequency re-

Fig. 14. Oblique sounding equipment, Ditton Park 1957 (Credit: STFC Rutherford Appleton Lab)

ceiver were developed at the RRS. Synchronism of the frequency synthesizers, the transmitter pulser and the time-base display at the receiver, several thousand kilometres away were achieved by high stability crystal clocks. Fig. 14 shows the equipment for this system at RRS, Ditton Park in 1957, with LTJ Martin (white coat) and EDR Shearman at right by the ex-wartime MB2 transmitter (much modified).

Post-war Commemorations

From the numerous post-war events, set up from time to time to mark the contributions to national defence made by the early British radar workers and the numerous progressive advances in the understanding of ionospheric phenomena, the following are worthy of particular notice:

1971. RAF stamp cover signed by
A.F. Wilkins and three other early workers on radar
(Described below by Dr J W King, former scientist at Ditton Park and philatelist)
'Many organisations, including the RAF, produce souvenir stamp covers relating to events which they wish to commemorate and which they ask various people to sign. The RAF produced a series of 90 covers which was called "The Co-ordinated Series", and the covers were numbered from C1 to C90. Cover Number C6 was issued on 30 November 1971 to commemorate the 25th Anniversary of the Inspectorate of Radio Services and the RAF felt it appropriate to ask four people who had worked on radar in Suffolk to sign the cover. One of the people who autographed the C6 covers (of which 256 were issued) was A.F. Wilkins. The 256 covers were then numbered C6c, and one is reproduced here. Many of the people working at Orfordness and Bawdsey Manor used the Bawdsey Ferry to travel to work and so the covers are franked on the back by the Bawdsey Ferry postmark. The names of the four people who signed the cover are given on an RAF card, one of which was enclosed with each cover. The C6c covers were issued by RAF Medmenham and flown on a round trip to inspect the radio equipment at Gibraltar, Malta, and Cyprus before returning to Medmenham on 10 December 1971, after which they were franked at Bawdsey Ferry on 17 December 1971. The C6 covers bore one of the radar stamps issued in1967 by the Post Office in their "British Discovery and Invention" series. See Figs. 15, 16 and 17.

The erection of a permanent stone memorial near Weedon, Northants
This memorial is close to the spot from which the 'Daventry Experiment' was conducted by Wilkins on 26 February 1935. It was unveiled on Battle of Britain Day, 15 September 2001 by Arnold Wilkins's widow, Nancy, in the presence of appropriate local dignitaries, local citizens and many wartime radar workers both ex-service and civilian. Brief speeches in appreciation of the value of radar in wartime were made by Jane Brackley, Public Relations Adviser to Qinetiq (the defence company descended from the wartime TRE) and by Tim Boswell, the MP for Daventry & District. See Figs 20, 21 and 22

Mrs Wilkins, having been introduced to the audience by the organiser of the event, Rex Boys, began by drawing attention, in a fine speech, to his central

Fig. 15. The front of RAF cover No. C6c (Credit: Dr J W King)

Fig. 16. The rear franked cover of RAF cover No. C6c (Credit: Dr J W King)

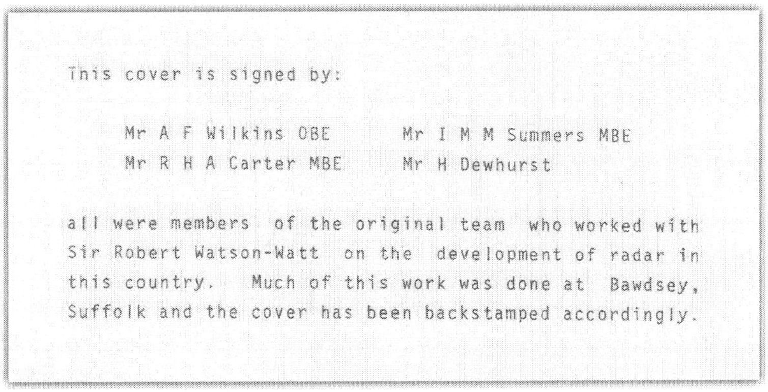

This cover is signed by:

Mr A F Wilkins OBE   Mr I M M Summers MBE

Mr R H A Carter MBE   Mr H Dewhurst

all were members of the original team who worked with Sir Robert Watson-Watt on the development of radar in this country. Much of this work was done at Bawdsey, Suffolk and the cover has been backstamped accordingly.

Fig. 17. The card enclosed in RAF cover No. C6c (Credit: Dr J W King)

Fig. 18. Retired ex-Ditton Park scientific staff and friends gathered outside
Ditton Manor on Saturday September 5th 2009. (Credit: John Reed.)

Fig. 19. The First Step - A small reproduction of the Painting by Roy Huxley
depicting the Daventry experiment 26-02-1935

81

Fig. 20. View of the
Memorial as seen
from the road
(Credit: Dr J W King)

Fig. 21. 'Close-up view of
words on the Memorial'
(Credit: Dr J W King)

Fig. 22. Near Weedon. notable visitors at the unveiling of the Memorial

From left to right:
Rex Boys, organiser;
Keith Mason,
Chairman of the Stowe-IX-Churches Parish Meeting;
Jane Bailey, QinetiQ;
Nancy Wilkins;
Tim Boswell, MP for Daventry;
Denis Brodie, landowner
(Credit: Mr Donald Tomlin)

Fig. 23. Ditton Park 2009. Tea cake designed to recapture the style of the original wooden buildings used for many years to accommodate technical staff in offices and laboratories. Initials on the rooftops recall the progressive changes in the station's title from RRS to RSRS and finally to Appleton Laboratory.
(Credit: Dr Paul Dickinson.)
(Cake supplied by Cake Expectations by Jo'lyn of Oxford.)

Fig. 24. Ionospheric scientists at Ditton Park, 1981'.
From left to right:
W R Piggot,
A F Wilkins,
J A Ratcliffe,
W J G Beynon.
(Credit: STFC Rutherford Appleton Lab.)

Fig. 25. Arnold Wilkins surrounded by long-service staff and retirees when he unveiled the plaque at Ditton Park, 1978. (Watson-Watt's old office in background).
(Credit: STFC Rutherford Appleton Lab.)

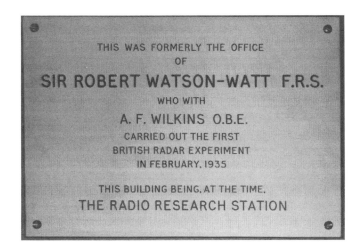

THIS WAS FORMERLY THE OFFICE
OF
SIR ROBERT WATSON-WATT F.R.S.
WHO WITH
A. F. WILKINS O.B.E.
CARRIED OUT THE FIRST
BRITISH RADAR EXPERIMENT
IN FEBRUARY, 1935

THIS BUILDING BEING, AT THE TIME,
THE RADIO RESEARCH STATION

Fig. 26. Close-up of the wording on the plaque. (Credit: STFC Rutherford Appleton Lab.)

Fig. 27. A F Wilkins, having just unveiled the Watson-Watt/Wilkins plaque, at Ditton Park, 1978. (Credit; STFC Rutherford Appleton Lab.)

Fig. 28. 'Nancy Wilkins
speaking before
dedicating the memorial
seat and table'
(Credit: Dr J W King)

Fig. 29. 'Memorial seat
and table, Ditton Park
2004' (Credit: Dr Paul
Dickinson)

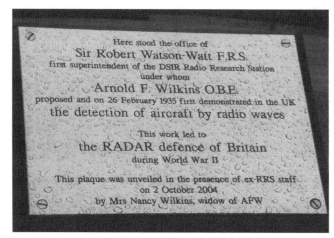

Here stood the office of
Sir Robert Watson-Watt F.R.S.
first superintendent of the DSIR Radio Research Station
under whom
Arnold F. Wilkins O.B.E.
proposed and on 26 February 1935 first demonstrated in the UK
the detection of aircraft by radio waves

This work led to
the RADAR defence of Britain
during World War II

This plaque was unveiled in the presence of ex-RRS staff
on 2 October 2004
by Mrs Nancy Wilkins, widow of AFW

Fig. 30. Close-up of
plaque on memorial
table, including
raindrops due to
sudden intense and
unexpected rainstorm!
(Credit: Dr Paul Dickinson)

part in the memorial project. The whole idea was his, and he alone had managed everything including the organisation of funds from Qinetiq and from private sources, plus the necessary applications for legalities such as planning permission etc. Nancy, 'overjoyed to praise the work of radar workers in wartime, from brilliant scientists to newest recruits' then unveiled the monument 'To the Birth of Radar'.

Sadly, Rex Boys – wartime RAF 'radio' (radar) mechanic and postwar BBC engineer has since died. To his many friends this handsome memorial serves also as a continuing reminder of his remarkable achievement and his support for CHiDE and DEHS over several years.

The memorial is located at National Grid Ref. SP 651556 at the side of the minor road running from Bugbrooke to Litchborough and is accessible from the A5 at a point approximately 5 miles north of Towcester.

Ditton Park

The following section contains a short history of Ditton Park, the home of the original Radio Research Station, compiled with contributions and help kindly provided by Dr Paul Dickinson, formerly a member of the scientific staff.

Ditton Park, Slough, (situated between Datchet and Langley, N side of M4 near Jct 5), has been a notable centre for many developments in radio technology and its applications from the early 1920s until 1981 when this work was transferred to the larger Rutherford Laboratory at Chilton, near Harwell, Oxfordshire. In those sixty years it became the happy home of many scientists and engineers and has resulted in reunions and commemorative gatherings from time to time, some of which are described below following a brief outline of the site's evolution.

The Park has existed since at least 1066 in the hands of the nobility. In 1331 Edward III granted license to the then owner John de Molyns to fortify "his mansun at Ditton". The moated manor house, surrounded by generous parkland, passed down to the Montagu family until, during the Great War, the Manor was compulsorily purchased by the Admiralty. The Manor House and Moat cost £20,000 in 1917 and the Admiralty paid a further £24,000 in 1919 for rest of the Park.

Scientific research arrived in Ditton Park in 1921 when The Admiralty converted the Manor into the Admiralty Compass Observatory (ACO). Small groups of scientists moved into the North and West Parks to undertake, for the Admiralty, certain experimental work on Radio Direction Finding which was hardly possible at the National Physical Laboratory, Teddington. Ditton Park provided adequate open space for aerials and the necessary freedom from electrical and magnetic interference. This move, of the ACO, was at the instigation, in 1920, of Sir Henry Jackson, Admiral of the Fleet, the first Chairman of the Radio Research Board of the DSIR (Department of Scientific and Industrial Research). The Board included founder member Ernest Rutherford and, from 1926 to 1939, one of his protégés Edward Appleton.

In 1924 the work at Ditton Park expanded when it became home also to the Meteorological Office's Wireless Station, transferred from Aldershot where research had been conducted into atmospherics and the location of thunderstorms under its leader, Robert Watson Watt. At first a large hut and tall radio mast were erected for them in the North Park but sadly soon destroyed completely by fire which defied the efforts of two brigades. A new set of buildings erected in the South Park remained until after 1982.

In 1927 Ditton Park was formally established as the Radio Research Station (RRS), mentioned frequently in these pages. Watson Watt became the Superintendent of the station until his transfer, early in wartime, to the Air Ministry following his overall leadership of the initial radar work. The RRS, as part of the DSIR, continued with direction-finding, field strength and upper atmosphere research. In particular, the ionised layer of the atmosphere (named in 1926 by Watson Watt the "ionosphere") was systematically monitored at RRS starting in 1931 using a pulsed RF sounder (ionosonde).

To this day ionosondes are used world-wide and the Slough data set, continuing at RAL is one of the longest upper atmosphere data sets available to science. The principle of the ionosonde, pulsed RF sounding, was seminal in the development of radar.

In 1965, when the DSIR was succeeded by the new Science Research Council (SRC), the RRS became the Radio and Space Research Station. This name reflected the growing scientific importance of instrumentation flown on balloons, rockets and satellites, fields in which the RSRS made substantial contributions. In 1973 the then Minister of Science, Margaret Thatcher, renamed it the Appleton Laboratory. In 1981 the SRC closed down the site and transferred the work to the Rutherford Laboratory, to form the Rutherford Appleton Laboratory (RAL) at Chilton. And now, at the time of this writing (2010), the archives of the RRS are held in the Space Science and Technology Department of RAL.

In 1982 Ditton Park was sold to Calor Gas, while the ACO remained in the Manor. In 1997 the entire Park including the Manor was sold to Computer Associates, who have carefully restored Ditton Manor but removed and landscaped all trace of the radio work.

With such a long, varied and successful involvement in so many branches of radio technology, it is not surprising that Ditton Park continues to hold the interest and affection of those who served there or had connections with the work.

Events at Ditton Park

1978

The unveiling, by Arnold Wilkins, former Deputy Director, of a plaque marking the location of Watson-Watt's office. The wooden building has since been demolished, but the plaque has been preserved and is retained in a prominent position on the wall of the foyer in the main building of European Headquarters of Computer Associates, in Ditton Park. See Figs. 25, 26 and 27.

1981

A commemoration of 50 years from 1931 when Sir Edward Appleton had pioneered the world's first ionospheric observatory, at the RRS. This event was attended by a number of renowned ionospheric scientists who watched an hourly observation of the ionosphere being recorded at Ditton Park - see Fig. 24.

2004

The occasion of a major staff reunion when an excellent speech was given by Nancy, the widow of A F Wilkins, who later that day dedicated a new garden seat, and table to the memory of Watson-Watt and Wilkins – see Figs. 28, 29 and 30.

2009

The most recent Ditton Park reunion took place on Saturday 5 September 2009 (when compilation of this book was in its final stages). Fig. 18 shows over 90 visitors assembled before lunch in front of Ditton Manor. This elegant building, built in 1871 to replace a similar previous house destroyed by fire in 1812, is set in the attractive 200 acre Ditton Park estate of typical English parkland. It has been the property of Computer Associates since 1997. The vastness of the estate has also enabled CA to build their European Headquarters in striking modern style but without encroaching at all upon the historical setting of the Manor and its delightful surroundings. History is the keyword; not only the sixty years of pioneering scientific work by the Radio Research Station (under its successive titles already mentioned), but the much longer involvement in the park itself by English nobility and royalty from the year 1066. In 1917, during the Great War, the entire estate, including the Manor was compulsorily purchased by the Admiralty under the Defence of the Realm Act.

The Manor is superbly maintained – as are the surrounding lawns and gardens – and it has become CA's executive suite for functions such as conferences and similar events. The company, aware of the contributions made on its site to modern science, is kindly pleased to permit these periodical reunion visits by ex-employees and their close family members.

Fig. 23 shows the commemorative cake specially made for the 2009 reunion, before being sliced and gleefully distributed to all present.

Interview with Arnold Wilkins
at his home on 2nd May 1983
Professor E.D.R. Shearman

Professor E D R Shearman has kindly provided us with the notes of a personal conversation with Arnold Wilkins when they were preparing the IEE Seminar entitled 'The History of Radar Development to 1945' held at Savoy Place on 11 June 1985. Together with Colin Pidd of RSRE Malvern, they were planning a joint paper on 'The UK Chain Home Radar System'. Unhappily, Wilkins was too ill to attend and died in August 1985.

We have included most of the conversation since it illuminates many points made in the Memoirs. In the main, the discussion focused around two accounts of the Chain Home, one by Sean Swords (Ref. 1) and the other by Bruce Neale (Ref. 2). The latter had appeared in the *GEC Journal of Research* and was subsequently re-published by the IEE (Ref. 3) in the volume based on the Seminar.

However, CH was not the sole subject discussed. There are references to a part of Wilkins's post-war 'Swords into Ploughshares' project, when both he and Professor Shearman had been involved in using wartime CH equipment and techniques to analyse long-distance HF radio propagation via the ionosphere—a pre-war interest to which Wilkins had returned with enthusiasm. With a rotating Yagi aerial, a modified MB2 transmitter, a special receiver and PPI, it was possible to display back-scatter from illuminated areas of the earth at ranges up to some 6000 kilometres in all directions, and thus determine the optimum HF wavelength and times of day for communication. (That is a highly fascinating subject, well deserving of attention, but it is beyond the scope of this present book.)

The Interview

EDRS   I was reading in Sean Swords's very useful account (Ref. 1), the two memoranda that went from Watson-Watt to Wimperis for the Tizard Committee. The second memorandum mentions the results from the initial tests that were done at Orfordness, which seemed to lead to the whole shape of the Chain. I just noted them down here:

                 The Daventry Experiment was in March 1935 (AFW: 'February 26th') followed by the Orford Experiments; was that in May? (AFW: 'they began on May 14th') and some of the conclusions are quoted in this second memorandum. It says that the early attainment of long ranges does not seem practical under 25m wavelength for the time being.

                 So that with the technology that was readily available, you were thinking of frequencies round about 12 MHz or so?

AFW   Yes that's right, that's what we worked on at the time.

EDRS   Then the subsequent history was the extension of the frequency range upwards?

AFW   Yes, we seemed to keep dividing the wavelength by two.

EDRS   And another conclusion is that the height of the aerials was important, that range varied as the square root of height, so that 200-ft masts on a 50-ft cliff would give a valuable improvement. And then, another recommendation is for a chain of transmitters, so that the name 'Chain' emerged at that stage?

AFW   Yes, that's right.

EDRS   Were there any other things leading to the shape of the Chain that came out early, like that?

AFW   Yes; well, of course, the height-finding was one thing, because the first proposal was that height should be measured by measuring the phase difference from the currents produced in two horizontally-spaced aerials.

EDRS   But you had done some work on that sort of thing before?

AFW   Yes, I had. That, in fact, was widely used and the first time height had been measured it was done using that method. Of course the snag with it was that you had to know the bearing of the aircraft and that was the very weak point. We didn't expect that direction finding could be as accurate as all that. And then we thought up this other system, with one aerial above the other, which was independent of bearing.

EDRS   And those experiments began in September 1935?

AFW   In September, that's right. It was the horizontal spacing system that I worked on then.

EDRS   I noticed, in Sean's account and in Bruce Neale's account, the use of a goniometer connected to the upper and lower aerials to measure height. When did that emerge? Did that come later on or was that concept there earlier?

AFW   That was there quite early. In fact we used it for the direction finding and that was one of the bonuses really in the height finding that with the currents being in phase in the two aerials, we could use the goniometer. And so from the operator's point of view it was the same sort of operation that had to be used.

EDRS   And it worked without too much ellipsing, did it?

AFW   Oh yes, it was very good.

EDRS   Did it depend on site at all? At Bawdsey you were using a sea re-flection-point.

AFW   Yes.

EDRS   And yet I remember you saying to me that in a way it was better to have a sloping foreground, like there was at Hillhead. Was that so you got the first beam lower down for long range?

AFW   It may have been that. I don't know that it was very important though.

That choice of the goniometer for the Direction Finding was a very interesting point. I think it was one of the very big mistakes we made and if you look at that memorandum of Watson-Watt's, you'll see that he puts forward the Cathode Ray Direction Finder (CRDF), which you would expect him to, wouldn't you? (Watson-Watt had pioneered the CRDF to locate the lightning discharges which were the source of atmospherics.)

We should have used it, because at the time of the V2's, when we had these CRDF's made up at Farnborough, they did the whole job very quickly and made a beautiful job of it. I remember operating one of those sets as a direction finder and you could read the bearings more accurately.

EDRS   So it was not only faster, it was more accurate?

AFW   Yes, what you had to do was to turn a knob, which was the counter-part of the goniometer control. You turned this knob until a cursor line coincided with the major axis of the ellipse. It was easier to do and you got a more accurate reading than swinging a gonio to get a minimum.

EDRS I think it is mentioned somewhere— probably in Watson-Watt's introduction to the Radiolocation Convention—that there was never time to do it earlier on.

AFW Well, I wouldn't think that was strictly correct. What happened was that Bainbridge-Bell, who was a CRDF expert, was sent back to Slough to start the development of the CRDF at these frequencies and he was not at all keen on the job. He didn't think it was possible, in fact. He didn't think it would be stable enough at such high frequencies.

EDRS It had been done at a few kilohertz, presumably, for atmospherics location.

AFW Yes, but it had been done at megahertz as well because the set I used for the Daventry experiment was such a set and I found it stable enough. But he didn't seem to accept that and then we relieved him of one half of the receiver for a special experiment and he never got it back.

  But later on, a fellow called Fereday, from the Station, he made one and it was very good indeed.

EDRS Yes, it mentions that here. 'The prospectus proposed to use in radiolocation the instantaneous cathode ray direction finder which had been used in locating sources of atmospherics and which was adapted as a radio polarimeter for atmospherics.

That was for the polarization of a down-coming wave?

AFW Yes, that's right.

EDRS 'It was left in abeyance for some years, but it was brought to a successful conclusion by Dr. Fereday at TRE. It was shown in a service trial in fully operational conditions to give a higher rate of reporting than the standard CH system. It did not mature early enough in the combat to justify the demand which its general production would have made on manufacturing and installation facilities.'

  Would you go along with that?

AFW I certainly would, yes.

EDRS But it was, in fact, used on V2's and I remember Eric Eastwood giving an account of that in a lecture to the IEE (Ref. 4).

AFW Do you remember that set? We had it in Hut 15 (at the Radio Research Station at Slough).

EDRS	That was your original set, wasn't it?
AFW	No, that was one of the sets that Farnborough made for detecting the V2.
EDRS	I thought that the one that stood in the corner of Hut 15 was the equipment that you did the experiment at Daventry with?
AFW	It may have been.
EDRS	I think it was and then it was refurbished in the workshop and presented to the Science Museum.
AFW	Yes, that's right.
EDRS	I am not sure that I saw one of those Farnborough equipments.
AFW	Anyhow, it was a very big thing in the middle of the hut and they used it for years. In fact, I think it was used for that oblique frequency-change job.
EDRS	The equipment that was used when I was there was a Plessey naval receiver, which was a further development along that line.
AFW	Yes, that's right.
EDRS	Subsequently to those, Racal built a twin-channel receiver which we still use today.
AFW	Do you? I am interested to know that they did in the end produce something, because I remember going to see one of these Racal receivers, and I said, 'Why don't you make this into a direction finder with two of them?' They did do something, but I didn't see it.
EDRS	They produced it as a complete equipment with the local oscillators of one driving the mixers of the other. They had a cathode-ray tube display with a sense switch. The Services bought quite a few of them and they sold some to overseas organizations.

The trouble with those now is interesting—the people who knew how to line them up at Racal have all retired and nobody has the skills required and the technology has moved on. So we are finding it very difficult to keep those old sets going and now more modern receivers have come along and it is possible to couple two of these together quite easily. You don't have much trouble if you take two of the receivers and common the oscillators together. They seem to be very stable now with digital frequency synthesisers and filters. I think now they have got the production to the point where it is much easier to make a twin-channel receiver than it was in those days.

Anyhow, going back to your original Daventry experiment, what |

was the actual set-up of the antennas there to null out the ground wave?

AFW   Well, the thing about that experiment was that the whole thing had to be done in a devil of a hurry so that there was no possibility of making new gear and I didn't see why one should. All I had to do was to lift one of those CRDF receivers and then we had a phase-shifter, which I made with my own hands. All you had to do was to set up two parallel aerials, one aerial connected to one receiver and the other aerial taken to the input of the phase-shifter with its output connected to the other receiver. Then the receivers were commoned somewhere along the receiver chain. It was very good; it cancelled the ground wave completely.

EDRS   So similar principles were used for height-finding on the Chain Home.

AFW   Yes, you could measure the angle of elevation down to a phenomenally low angle. I forget exactly what it was—a quarter of a degree according to my memory.

EDRS   That's at what frequency, 50 or 60 MHz?

AFW   Well, it was 6.74 metres (44.5 MHz) and at a coastal station.

EDRS   It seems from the illustrations that, for the transmitter, there were four aerial bays for the four different frequencies and for each one there was a main array and a gap-filler at a lower height. For the receiving system there were three aerials at different heights. The top pair were used for accurate height-finding, but there would be an ambiguity. So then the bottom pair would be used to resolve the ambiguity. Were they used as a normal thing? Were you frequently switching between the two?

AFW   Oh yes, all the time.

EDRS   So if you were looking at distant aircraft to get greater height accuracy you would use the top two, but you would do a check with the bottom two to avoid ambiguity. Then the need for transmitter aerial gap-filling occurred when you were looking at high angle aircraft and then you would switch to the other transmitter antenna. Were there gaps on the receive system too? Say, if you were using an aerial at a particular height, would you not get an interferometer pattern on that?

AFW   Oh yes, yes.

EDRS   It shows here three vertically-spaced pairs of aerials at respectively 215ft, 95ft and 45ft. So that's approximately half and half again.

AFW	That's right.
EDRS	But it looks from this diagram that the upper and lower pairs had crossed dipoles and switched reflectors, whereas the 95ft pair each had only one dipole and reflector. That was used for height-finding and not for direction finding?
AFW	Yes, I would say that.
EDRS	Did the vertically-spaced pairs constitute two-stacked arrays to give further gain?
AFW	Yes.
EDRS	And were those aerials coupled together by twin feeders within a single coaxial shield?
AFW	No, they were two single core coaxials.
EDRS	Did the screens have to be bonded together?
AFW	Yes they did.
EDRS	Somewhere, in one of the Radiolocation Convention papers, I saw the azimuthal errors of the system at an early stage, compared with the much better performance at a later stage. Did there have to be some development work to reduce the errors due to dipole connections and that sort of thing?
AFW	Yes, there was a lot of activity there. I think the big trouble that was never really overcome was the capacitative coupling between the two dipoles via the reflector.
EDRS	Did that upset the symmetry?
AFW	Yes, we must have been very lucky in those very first installations, in that you had the reflectors further away from the dipoles, so that the coupling wasn't all that big. It was all done very rapidly, you see, and we didn't really have time to bother with tests before putting it into operation.
EDRS	But it wasn't such a bad system really, was it?
AFW	No, not at all.
EDRS	It did the job, though there had to be calibrations.
AFW	Yes, there did.
EDRS	Did that calibration vary significantly with time or did those capacitances remain fairly stable?

AFW   It seemed to me remarkably stable. I don't know how often they calibrated it.

By the way there was one interesting thing that I have been kicking myself for, ever since 1940. I went round some of these stations and inspected them and I got a very high opinion of the quality of Pevensey station. They operated it for quite a long time: in fact they were trying to bring about interceptions at night.

But on one occasion, the Germans were coming in on a straight line from somewhere in France to London and they were crossing the coast—I expect it would be somewhere near Beachy Head—all at the same height and all were fully separated. It was a marvellous opportunity to study the characteristics of the aerials. I remember we had selected the aerials for a medium height system—230 and 80 we called it. We got these echoes spread out along the time base and you could see the gaps at the right places and then switched on the gap-filler and the gaps would disappear.

It was a beautiful performance and it proved what I always used to say whenever I contemplated the radar system, you could always rely on the aerials and polar diagrams for effects like this and by George, it was so on this occasion. I was kicking myself that I didn't have a camera. If I had that as a record it would have been a very good thing.

EDRS   Of course, Pevensey was a very good site. I remember going down there to learn about the techniques so that we could run the Hillhead station. We would travel about this absolutely dead flat land to get to the site.

So when was it that one of those high towers was first built? Was that at Bawdsey?

AFW   Yes, we started in 1936 and finished in 1937.

EDRS   So you moved to Bawdsey by 1936.

AFW   Yes, March 1936.

EDRS   And what was the idea of this move? Was it to be nearer to the important area, close to London?

AFW   No the foundations at Orford were unsuitable.

EDRS   So the high transmitter towers were put up at Bawdsey, were they?

AFW   Yes.

EDRS   Two or Four?

AFW   I think they put the four up right away there.

EDRS	I remember seeing four towers at Bawdsey in later years, which meant, presumably, three arrays (if strung between them) and yet there were four towers on the receive site. What was the idea of that? Or was there to be more than one array between some of the towers?
AFW	Well the arrays were going to be between the cantilevers on one tower.
EDRS	What, either side of the mast?
AFW	Yes.
EDRS	But then you could have four pairs. But they are shown here strung between the masts. Is this picture (Figure 31) not right then?
AFW	No, I think this (Figure 32, right-hand drawing) is the system we put up (end-driven horizontal dipoles suspended between a single tower and a triatic strung vertically between cantilevers). This one (Figure 31) is the Marconi System (dipoles strung between adjacent towers).
EDRS	So yours were between the cantilevers? There are two arrays there, one near the top and one near the bottom.
AFW	That's right. They were rather unusual.
EDRS	Seem to be driven from one side.
AFW	They were, yes.
EDRS	So you got a high impedance.
AFW	Yes—5,000 Ohms.
EDRS	So there were a number of high impedance taps end-feeding the dipoles feeding approximately equal power. But what happened at the top? Was there any power left over at the top or was that short circuited? Perhaps there was a standing wave there, was there?
AFW	I don't remember anything being done at the top; there were just 5,000 ohm loads half a wavelength apart. Watson-Watt's idea was that we would be able to get at the things to adjust them and get the minimum backward radiation.
EDRS	And there was a reflector curtain behind.
AFW	Yes, Oh yes.
EDRS	But the West Coast aerials?
AFW	They were Koomans arrays, weren't they.
DRS	And did they have reflectors?

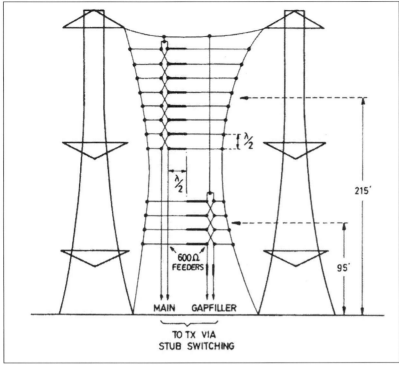

Fig 31 CH transmitter array (Credit: BAE Systems)

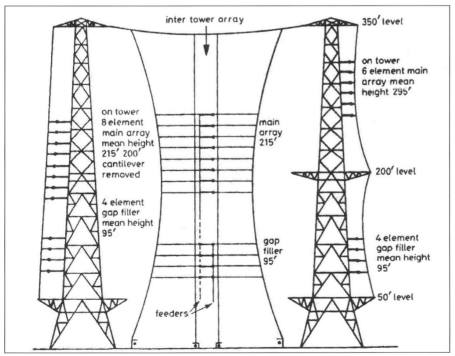

**Fig. 32. CH transmitter antenna arrays in various configurations
(Credit: BAE Systems)**

AFW   They all had reflectors.

EDRS   In all of them there were four of these masts, weren't there?

AFW   They were a waste of money, really; we didn't need them. Yes, the original idea was to have four separate wavelengths to counter jamming. I can't remember ever having more than two at any one station. This station up here at High Street: that had two wavelengths. It had one in the 40 MHz region and another about 50 MHz.

EDRS   So the between-towers version must have been a Mark II then?

AFW   Oh yes! It was a post-war thing.

EDRS   Now, about the transmitters. You got in touch with Metropolitan Vickers. How did this come about?

AFW   Well, they were making the MB1 and I expect they were invited to continue the development and that led to the MB2. To get even higher power—I expect it was Dodds—suggested the CED (continuously evacuated demountable) valves. It was a very great success.

EDRS   They were made for broadcasting purposes, weren't they?

AFW   I don't know. The only place where I saw them was Rugby Radio Station: they were used in a long-wave set.

EDRS   Tetrodes, they were, weren't they?

AFW   Yes, that's right.

EDRS   Presumably tetrodes enabled you to get a bigger swing at the anodes without a phenomenal drive power; if the anode swings down to the grid potential in a triode, it takes a lot of current, so needs a lot of drive power.

AFW   I don't think the drive stage was very powerful.

EDRS   It was a curious valve for the oscillator, wasn't it? A double tetrode strapped as an unbalanced valve.

AFW   I don't remember that. It's written up in the IEE Radiolocation Convention paper by Whelpton.

EDRS   Yes I have an abstract here—'Metre-Wave Transmitters for Warning and Aircraft Location', by R V Whelpton and J M Dodds.

EDRS   One thing that interests me is how the design of the typical Chain Home station emerged from those early experiments. Did you write those memoranda, Arnold?

AFW   Watson-Watt and I put our heads together.

EDRS   A joint effort.

AFW   Yes.

EDRS   In the second of those memoranda, it mentions the concept of 200ft masts on a cliff. So that idea did emerge. The idea of a chain and the name 'Chain' was in there too. What about the idea of the floodlight transmit and the direction-finding? Were other things considered? Were beams considered at that stage?

AFW   No.

EDRS   They weren't really viable at those low frequencies?

AFW   That's right. We never really considered them.
The direction-finding and the height-finding had been settled. The masts for the receiving side had been more or less settled. It was very interesting; Watson had very great luck with those wooden towers. He had seen them in Germany; some of the German Broadcasting Stations used them. He seemed to me to be determined to have those and then we found that we could get them for £2,400 each. We wanted a higher mast for the transmitting aerials to get the mean height the same as the mean height of the receiving aerials. The Ministry of Works people told him he could have a 320ft steel tower, with those cantilever arms, for the same price as one wooden tower—and that was wonderful. And that was how that came about.
Personally, I wouldn't have had those.

EDRS   Wouldn't you?

AFW   No, I wouldn't have had those. I preferred the ordinary guyed masts—

EDRS   —which were used later—

AFW   —on the West Coast sites. Yes. In fact, when the Chain was refurbished, in 1947 I think it was.

EDRS   or was it later, because the Radio Research Station were ejected from Hillhead for the refurbishment in the 1950's, I think.

AFW   That would be when there was a threat of war with Russia.
Yes, they then put up aerials suspended between the masts. And put up the power.

EDRS   Yes, using the VT114a instead of the original large continuously evacuated demountable valves, which greatly reduced the maintenance effort. (The VT114a was a version, with cooling fins added, of the VT114 air-cooled tetrode, both of which had thoriated tungsten cathodes with 70 amps peak emission).

AFW   Yes, that's right.

EDRS   But the old transmitter got up to—I remember a figure of 600 kW, but it gives a figure of 750 in Sean Swords' book.

AFW   No! 600 kW is the figure I remember. It started off as 250 and then 600 later on.

EDRS   Coming back to the transmitting aerials, Sean Swords (Ref2) shows both the types of array you mentioned. He says here 'that a cause of unwanted backward radiation was the excitation of the steel elements of the supporting tower. There was of course considerable coupling between these and the elements of the array and it was found that quite large currents were flowing in the cantilevers'.

AFW   Did I ever tell you that story about backward radiation from aerials? It was soon after we moved from Bawdsey to Dundee and were joined by a couple of young gentlemen, Martin Ryle and I forget the other man's name. These people were working under me at the time and I got them to do some model aerial tests at centimetre wavelengths. In the course of their work, I think Rowe must have spotted them and he talked to them about what they were doing and they showed him the polar diagram of the aerial they were working on. Rowe got hold of this thing and came down to me with these two chaps and said: 'look here, Wilkins, these two men have just joined us and see what they have got, far, far better results than you've got and you've been here all these years.'

  Their polar diagram was a plot of power and he was reading it as voltage.

References

1. S S Swords, *Technical History of the beginnings of Radar*, IEE Peter Peregrinus London, 1986, Fig 5.19, p.227. (Shows various transmitting antenna configurations.)

2. B T Neale, 'CH—The first operational radar', *GEC Journal of Research*, **3**, No 2, 1985, pp 73-83. (More photographs than Ref.3)

3. B T Neale, 'CH—The first operational radar', in *Radar Development to 1945*, Russell Burns (Ed), IEE Peter Peregrinus, London, 1988, pp 132–150.

4. E. Eastwood, Inaugural Address as President, IEE, *Proc. IEE*, **120**, No 1, Jan 1973.

A brief acquaintance with Arnold Wilkins
by Colin Latham

It was fifty years after Arnold Wilkins's Daventry experiment of February 1935 that I first met him. To commemorate the jubilee of British radar the BBC was planning 'The Long Watch'—a programme in the scientific series 'QED', and had sought the help of Marconi Radar Systems Ltd.

In consequence, on a wintry morning in early 1985, I and my colleague Bruce Neale—both Marconi radar engineers—set out by road from Chelmsford to Arnold's home at Saxstead Green in Suffolk. We were to collect him and go on to Northamptonshire to meet the BBC team from London at the Crossroads Motel, Weedon, before visiting and filming the site of the Daventry Experiment.

Bruce and I were looking forward to meeting Arnold. It was an opportunity for us since we had worked on Chain Home radar in the RAF in wartime and were ourselves involved in the design of post-war radars. How would this genuine pioneer regard us? Friendly perhaps, or condescending and reserved, as some inventors and pioneers regrettably tend to be, to those who follow?

We need not have worried. From the moment we collected Arnold we knew we'd found a friend. Guessing that we'd need to talk on the journey, we were travelling in a Marconi chauffeur-driven car so were able to relax in comfort while our driver pressed on through depressingly worsening weather.

Arnold spoke to us in engineer-to-engineer terms and clearly enjoyed a receptive and understanding audience for his tales of technical and administrative problems in the early days of radar. I shall never forget his frequent references to Watson-Watt. Neither laudatory nor derogatory, they were laced with humorous chuckles as if he were constantly amused by the memory of his former boss's antics. It was as if a fond relative were divulging the exploits and quirks of a respected but slightly eccentric family member who had always needed to be gently humoured. In successive anecdotes he referred either to 'Wattie' or to 'my uncle', and invariably with a smile or chortle.

We reached The Crossroads at Weedon safely despite the bad weather but during lunch snow began to fall and it was soon clear that filming would have to be postponed for another time. So we lingered on, chatting and reminiscing in comfort with Arnold and our BBC friends, before departing our different ways on the worsening roads. Although the return journey to Saxstead was slow, Bruce and I had no cause to complain: it gave us more time to become better acquainted with Arnold and to learn more about his 'uncle'.

From that day on, until his unexpected death on 7 August 1985, we were to meet Arnold again on several occasions, including his welcome appearance as Guest of Honour at the Marconi Radar Apprentice prize-giving ceremony in April of that year. From those meetings, spread over little more than half a year, together with correspondence with him on technical matters, Bruce and I knew that we had come to know a man of outstanding capability, integrity and wisdom. This view was endorsed when we received, through our Marconi office, a copy of a letter written by Lord Bowden of Chesterfield informing the Institution of Electrical Engineers of Arnold's death.

Lord (Vivian) Bowden, himself a highly qualified scientist, who had contributed to the science of radar and worked with Arnold in the early days of radar, wrote of him:

'He was a great man in his way. He played a most important part in the development of the Home Chain which saved us all at the time of the Battle of Britain. He was modest and unassuming; he was kind, able and something of an inspiration to everyone who knew him. He allowed Watson-Watt to take the credit for many of his own ideas. I remember that he always called Watt 'my uncle' and he never seemed to mind if Watt had all the public credit for some of his best ideas.'

Review and comments

It may well be that readers of this saga of Arnold Wilkins, noting his vital involvement in the early days of radar in the UK, are reaching the stage – in company with radar historians in general - of posing a pertinent question. The question is why, when he had successfully led the CH development team for some five years from 1935, did Wilkins not follow through as our senior radar scientist at one of the government's major technical establishments such as TRE? The answer, to which we shall return presently, lies in the unexpected rise of microwave engineering and its application to radar.

From his own reminiscences – and indeed from what his contemporaries have written – it is clear that although Watson Watt was the able and much-liked leader of Britain's first radar development phase it was only through Arnold's calm reflection on the death ray idea that radar development began when it did. Further, his simple Daventry experiment, set up so rapidly, was all that Watson Watt needed to sell the idea of aircraft detection by radio waves to the Air Ministry. Watson Watt, distinguished scientist as he was, became well known also for his abilities of persuasion.

It has been reported that when Watson Watt was transferred to the Air Ministry in May 1938 he was much missed by his staff at Bawdsey. Even so, it was realised that there was a real compensation: he would be in a prime position, with his persuasive manner, to draw attention to the advantages and possibilities of radar amongst those at the highest levels of national defence.

This kind of comment about W-W's energetic salesmanship, made so very frequently, leads inevitably to tedious comparisons with AFW's reserved manner and the question: who deserves the greater credit for radar's success? The answer, as stated earlier, is that their roles were entirely complementary, this firm conclusion coming not only from those who knew them in their prime but similarly from historians taking up the subject afresh. Let us take, as an example of the latter, the case of a mature student, Mr Tony Flux, reading for his second degree of MSc at Bournemouth University at the beginning of the 21st century. Entirely unfamiliar with the subject, he took on the task of researching, as a project for CHiDE and the Heritage Lottery Fund, the history of radar. He approached this in a professional manner, not just by studying all available literature but also by interviewing veterans as far as possible and visiting relevant museums and archival depositories including the GPO research establishment, Dollis Hill.

In his thesis this Mr Flux stated: 'It was Wilkins who introduced the point about some earlier (1931-2) problematical observations that the Post Office had noted. (GPO Report No. 233, 'Interference by Aeroplanes'). The engineers had observed disturbances to VHF reception when an aircraft flew in the vicinity of a radio receiver and Wilkins wondered if this phenomenon could be used to detect the presence of aircraft.' After summarising Watson Watt's prophetic memorandum to the Air Ministry, (accurately forecasting numerous possibilities for what later became known as 'radar'), this scientific researcher gave his own assessment of Watson Watt's role:

'Perhaps the real place in the story of radar that Watson Watt should occupy is that of choreographer or pioneer. Many of the principles involved: the mathematics – the physics of radio waves – the observation of the phenomenon of interference – the construction of VHF transmitters and receivers – the possible applications for reflected electromagnetic waves - the military applications for this technology – had all been explored by many other scientists from Germany, Italy, the USA, and England over the previous 50 years but it was Watson Watt who possessed the necessary perception to see the full potential of this science and the tenacity to push the whole issue through to a functional conclusion'.

It would be wrong however, to suggest that he "invented" 'radar'. Those who knew both Watson Watt and Wilkins, and have been consulted, agree that the above remarks are fair to both scientists.

From short waves to microwaves

While CH, working mainly on wavelengths of some 10 -15m, had been of unprecedented value for long-range early warning in 1940 it soon became clear that newer radars at even shorter wavelengths had significant advantages including detection at lower angles of elevation, improved bearing accuracy and more reliable height-finding. All this was becoming possible because of successive improvements in transmitting valve technology from about 1935 onwards. CHL radars used valves giving some hundreds of kilowatts of pulsed power at 1.5 metres wavelength but the most dramatic breakthrough by far was the availability of similar pulse powers at 10cm wavelength from cavity magnetrons following experiments at Birmingham University early in 1940 and intense development by GEC, Wembley. At first it was hard to believe that the relatively tiny magnetron could produce, at so short a wavelength, pulsed powers of the same order as the very much larger valves of a CH transmitter.

It was not the magnetron alone that comprised a microwave radar. Also necessary was the very rapid development of the associated equipment such as receivers and all the radio-frequency components, including the antenna. An entirely new raft of technology came into being at short notice and it must have been clear to Wilkins that, much as he had taken the lead in the development of CH, this new phase had moved from the domain of the traditional radio engineer to the realm of the advanced experimental scientist. Leading scientists from university research centres were appointed to Civil Service establishments developing radar for the armed services.

Wilkins was not one to push himself forward and it is easy to understand why, with radar technology stepping into new microwave fields, he preferred to accept the post in Ceylon where, among other things, he might exploit his own subject of long range radio propagation at more conventional wavelengths. It is appropriate at this point to review the state of commercial and public interest in wireless communications in 1931 when Arnold had joined the Radio Research Station.

Widespread interest in ionospheric reflection

Ever since the BBC had begun broadcasting from station 2LO in London near the end of 1922, and soon afterwards from other regional stations, more and more homes boasted receivers of one sort or another. At first many people began 'listening in' via headphones driven by 'crystal sets'. No amplification was provided for the incoming signal transmitted from a reasonably local radio station and usually picked up by a vast aerial in the garden. The sound in the headphones was only faint and usually demanded careful listening in quiet surroundings.

The attraction of 'listening to the wireless' became so popular that by 1930 many homes had progressed to valve receivers with loudspeakers and 'wireless sets' were beginning to be called 'radio receivers'. Valves needed power supplies to perform amplification and even up to the outbreak of war in 1939 some receivers were still battery-operated even though mains-driven sets had become available for some ten years. One effect of the availability of better receivers was the ease with which it became possible to listen to radio broadcasts from foreign countries.

Most radio sets in the 1930s received on Long and Medium wavebands. (The former 1000 – 2000m wavelength; the latter 200-500 m). Listeners found that by using the long waveband at any time of the day or night they could tune into the strong signal of the BBC National Programme from Daventry (later Droitwich) as well as a few continentals such as Radio Paris and Radio Luxembourg. Medium waves in daytime gave a few of the British regional stations and little else but as darkness approached and the evening drew on something magical happened - dozens of European stations came flooding in, many at great strength.

This was both a bonus and a problem: while it was wonderful to hear foreign programmes they could often be so powerful and numerous that reception of our own stations was spoiled at night by unwanted interference. The cause of this effect was well-known as being due to reflections of radio waves from regions of the earth's upper atmosphere which had been ionised by the sun. It was discussed in the press in general terms but in much more detail in scientific papers; also in the many journals that then catered for amateur radio experimenters who concentrated on wavelengths below 100 metres.

That newly explored region of the radio wave spectrum down to 10 metres was known as 'short waves' and from the mid-thirties many of the more up-market radio receivers covered three wavebands – Long, Medium and Short. From about 1936 there was much publicity along the lines of 'listen to America direct in your own home' but on the whole the public were slow to take much interest in short waves.

The value of radio amateurs ('Hams')

By contrast radio enthusiasts – and especially radio 'hams' (licensed to operate their own transmitters) - made great use of short waves. With their specialised equipment (often home-made) radio amateurs contributed much to a more complete understanding of how to make best use of the reflective characteristics of the upper regions of the atmosphere. Some members of the Radio Society of Great Britain made news achieving remarkable feats of radio contact with like-minded amateurs all over the world. Some leading individuals in the history of radio communication were themselves classified as "radio amateurs" in curious contrast to their main positions as professional scientists and engineers. One such was a young Italian experimenting in Britain around the turn of the 19th/20th centuries. His name was G. Marconi, later an Honorary Member of the RSGB, while in 1925 the President of the RSGB was Sir Oliver Lodge. So much for the term 'ham'!

Wavelengths below 10 metres were designated 'ultra short waves' though not, in the early 1930s, seriously exploited due to the non-availability of noise-free valves for reception at such high frequencies and effective valves for transmitting.

Commercial and national short wave users

The possibilities of world wide radio communication opened up as it was found that short wave propagation, using reflected sky waves, could be achieved around the globe over very long distances using only modest transmitter power provided that the optimum wavelength was used for the particular period of day or night. Commercial companies, on the whole using the Morse code, as well as national broadcasting organisations, such as the BBC with its broadcasts to the Empire, sought ways and means of scheduling their programmes and channels to best effect. Nowadays, with our man-made satellites we take good quality world-wide radio and TV relays for granted but in those days only the ionised regions were available to reflect radio signals. While this method was welcome it had the drawback that spurious changes in reflectivity depending upon the time of day, the season and even variations from year to year according to sun spot activity, made it difficult to be sure of reliable reception. Except under exceptionally favourable conditions short wave reception was rarely free from some fading and sometimes from severe distortion.

Experts who had studied these problems seriously were in demand. Arnold, who began his professional career at a period when this matter was of primary importance took to it with great enthusiasm so that by 1935, when the death ray question was asked, he had become one of the experts in radio wave propagation. He was then just the right man for the job of setting up a short wave radar system; but by 1941 others had become distinguished in the new microwave field.

Worldwide interest in radar – pre-war & wartime

In wartime our radar activities were cloaked in secrecy but Britain was not the only country so engaged. The principle of detection by reflected radio waves from a target such as a ship or aircraft had been postulated by many for some years and isolated experiments had been set up in several countries. Germany in particular had developed radars concentrating mainly on equipments of precision but of modest range for gun control and some progress was made elsewhere, notably in the USA.

This widespread interest in the possibilities of radar are well described in 'A Radar History of World War II' (Institute of Physics Publishing, 1999, Bristol and Philadelphia) by the late Louis Brown of the Carnegie Institute of Washington. He states a significant factor; 'Another very important difference distinguished the British approach to radar from that of other countries. Where foreign radar men had had to contend with moderate interest and weak support, British radar men received strong support from the highest level'. This is correct as a statement of policy despite justifiable grumbles, from those developing radar in the early days, about their lack of test gear and scientific instruments.

Dr Brown also observed that the high build-quality of German radar equipment in WW2 had its pros and cons. While it was reliable and painstakingly designed for easy replacement of individual units by largely non-technical military personnel it was not amenable to quick on-site modifications. By contrast British equipment – much more hastily designed and later brought up to date, when required, by radar mechanics of a high technical standard – was more adaptable to changing conditions in wartime.

The development of radar as a serious defensive measure, in which Britain's CH system was outstanding has, in the history of its evolution, a striking resemblance to the technically different development of the cavity magnetron and its rapid application to microwave radars. The development of radar itself and of the magnetron as a new powerful generator of very short radio waves were both conducted speedily and in utmost secrecy. Britain was ahead of the world with CH and with magnetron-powered radars.

The facts are that, immediately after the successful demonstration at Birmingham of a rudimentary cavity magnetron, development for production in quantity began at GEC Wembley. Also, work started at TRE on the design of microwave airborne radars and, with Admiralty scientists, on the first operational naval microwave radar, the Type 271. Meanwhile British cavity magnetron samples were supplied to the USA by the Tizard Committee to encourage American engineers to design microwave radars.

That was how it was, yet we are now learning that the concept of the cavity magnetron (not just the much older split anode magnetron with an external resonant circuit) was known in many countries and had, for years, been the subject of innumerable reports, proposals and patents! As with radar, many had thought of the idea and produced masses of paperwork; but no actual hardware of significance. Little real cavity magnetron success was achieved other than in France until thwarted by the German invasion. In the actual development of the cavity magnetron it is now clear that only Britain gave real support in terms of facilities and finance, enabling hardware for operational use to be manufactured without delay. In Japan, devices were produced and even experimental CW and pulsed radars were made but not deemed by the services to be necessary or useful.

A pitfall in technical histories

How curious it is, from these two examples, that achievements of undoubted success seem to be followed, inevitably, and about half a century later, by support for those who tried and yet, for whatever reasons, failed! While it is right and proper that such information be aired in the interests of technical history we must be aware that, if overdone, it could eventually distort the balance of history for future generations of students. They might wonder, for example, why we have made a fuss about the Birmingham cavity magnetron of 1940 when so many earlier papers and patents already existed? A better question for them might be along the lines of why none of those far-seeing prewar inventors ever produced a magnetron that worked well enough to lead to microwave radars in their own countries?

To return to CH itself, students might also wonder why Britain became so advanced in radar by 1939 when the possibility had been considered, universally, for years. It is to be hoped that this book will help to preserve the true history of the development of the world's first operational radar system for national defence and the parts played in its birth by Watson Watt, Arnold Wilkins and his enthusiastic hard-working team.

Radar and fighter control

As Adolf Galland rightly said, it was radar *and fighter control* that did the trick. Radar alone is not a defensive weapon; it is the fire power of gunnery that shoots the enemy down, and it is far more likely to be successful from an armed fighter aircraft in comparatively close proximity than from ground-based anti-aircraft fire. Hence the value of fighter control aided by radar, especially at night or in poor conditions of visibility.

Fortunately this was understood by a few high ranking and influential members of defence committees during the mid-1930s, notably Sir Henry Tizard, Lord Swinton and Air Marshal Sir Hugh Dowding, who - even while early warning by radar was merely an unproven possibility - set up an exercise known as the 'Biggin Hill Experiment'. (Against much opposition from some service chiefs who considered it a waste of time.)

It was feared that when radar-derived data on incoming raids became available, fighter pilots - so accustomed to making their own decisions while airborne - might find it find it hard to act upon instructions in their headphones from the ground. They, and their ground-based counterparts, would need to establish, agree and become familiar with procedures for transmitting radio messages from ground to air so that action could be taken as unambiguously and promptly as possible.

Consequently, a series of air exercises was set up at 32 Squadron, RAF Biggin Hill, during 1936-7 in which a system called 'Pipsqueak' stood in for the coming radar, yet to be operational. Pipsqueak used high frequency direction finding (HFDF) ground-based stations to locate (by intersection of measured bearings) the positions of aircraft carrying special air-to-ground transmitters. Such aircraft constituted a mock attacking force and their tracks were radioed, ground-to-air, to others from Biggin Hill acting as interceptors. Thus the basic operational procedures for interceptions by 'fighter control' were worked out and refined by the time war started in 1939 and radar detection of raiders had become a routine procedure.

Writing after the war, Air Marshal Sir Arthur McDonald concluded that but for the Biggin Hill exercises, and the lessons learned, the Battle of Britain would have been lost.

Arnold Wilkins in private life, during and after the war

It is clear from Arnold's memoirs, as well as from the recollections of those who worked with him in the early days, that he was continuously and heavily committed to radar development - to the exclusion of pretty well all else - for some five years from 1935. This was a demanding lifestyle, though by no means uncongenial since his team worked together enthusiastically, sharing the ups and downs of their experiments and trials. During the early part of that period, when activities were mainly at Orfordness, he took accommodation wherever it could be found - in hotels or 'digs' - but later when at Bawdsey he was able to make use of a room reserved for his use in his father's new home in Felixstowe. This was a happy coincidence since, on his father's retirement from teaching in Chester (c. 1937), Arnold's parents moved to Suffolk and arranged for the building of a house overlooking the seafront. With a garage, but no car themselves, they thoughtfully provided an inspection pit in it for Arnold's occasional use if required. (His interest in cars is shown on p. 35 where Watson Watt surprisingly makes a brave experiment that few car owners would care to try!)

By the start of the war in September 1939 the value of early warning by ground-based radar systems was no longer in doubt. Further developments and extensions continued throughout the war, designed and installed by vastly enlarged technical teams and resources. However this brought little easing of pressure on Arnold himself who was transferred to the Air Ministry at Bentley Priory, Stanmore, with the honorary rank of RAF Group Captain. During this period - prior to his being posted to Ceylon - he lived temporarily with his married sister, Louise, at her home in nearby Edgware where, also, a room was always willingly reserved for him.

It is no wonder then, with all those years of busy technical work amongst predominately male company, that Arnold did not find the opportunity to marry Nancy Broome until he was 42 in 1949. This was by contrast with most men who (especially, it is said, in wartime) tend to do so in their twenties. But a thoroughly happy marriage it was indeed, with a family of three daughters added in the 1950s. At last it must also have been a joy for him to have homes of his own - firstly near Slough while working at the Radio Research Station, Ditton Park and later on retirement at Saxstead Green in his beloved Suffolk.

For those of us at Marconi Radar Systems who came to know him during 1985 through preparations for the BBC's television series *THE SECRET WAR,* and his visit to the company in Chelmsford, his untimely death on August 5th, aged 78, was a great sadness. He was survived by Nancy who, before her death in 2011, often attended events commemorating the value of radar in wartime. In her eloquent speeches she gave much credit to her husband and his pioneering colleagues for their contribution to the defence of Britain. She also showed much helpful interest in the preparation of this book, gratefully acknowledged.

Throughout this book credit is given, repeatedly, to the efforts of the radar pioneers. But all their brilliance and industry would have counted for nothing in the decisive Battle of Britain had it not been for the bravery of our airmen, of whom, sadly, so many gave their lives.

Defence Electronics History Society

Much of the fascinating history described in The Birth of British Radar is of great interest to the members of the Defence Electronics History Society (DEHS). Colin Latham, editor and contributor to this revised edition, was the first Chairman of DEHS, and is a Life Member of the society. If you would like to find out more about DEHS aims, activities and publications, details are available on the website www.dehs.org.uk . Membership is open to all - simply download a membership application form from the website.

Since its inception in 1995, originally as the Friends of the Centre for the History of Defence Electronics (CHiDE), DEHS has played a valuable role in the study and public awareness of the history of defence electronics.

DEHS's remit is wide - from DC to light, from the earliest transmissions and detection of information to today's secure high-speed data links, from the earliest use of electronics in war to present day conflicts. These interests extend to the people who researched and developed electronic technology, those who build and maintain it, and those who use it.

DEHS organises lectures and symposia every year, mainly at the Defence Academy of the United Kingdom, Shrivenham. Papers presented at symposia are available as Proceedings. DEHS also produces a range of specialist publications. Members of DEHS receive a quarterly newsletter, containing feature articles and lively correspondence.

Dick Green
Secretary, DEHS
Oct 2011

www.dehs.org.uk